D1232069

(

VASCULAR DIFFERENTIATION
IN PLANTS

These Studies are designed to inform the mature
student—the undergraduate upperclassman and the
beginning graduate student—of the outstanding ad-
vances made in various areas of modern biology. The
books will not be treatises but rather will briefly sum-
marize significant information in a given field and
interpret it in terms of our current knowledge of the
rapidly expanding research findings within the life
sciences. Also it is hoped that the Studies will be of
interest to teachers and research workers.

BIOLOGY ⟵
STUDIES

Katherine Esau
University of California
Santa Barbara

VASCULAR DIFFERENTIATION IN PLANTS

Holt, Rinehart
and Winston
New York, Chicago,
San Francisco,
Toronto, London

preface

Studies on vascular tissues in their mature state have contributed greatly to our store of knowledge of the plant and its function. Thus, for example, comparative research on the vascular system, or on the tissues composing it, has played a large role in the development of taxonomic and evolutionary concepts. As another example, research on structure of the xylem as a water-conducting tissue, and of the phloem as a food-conducting tissue, has provided a basis for the formulation of concepts on the movement of materials in plants.

Reference to mature structure only does not, however, adequately characterize the plant as a living organism. The structure of the plant undergoes profound changes as it develops from its inception in the seed, and many aspects of the earlier structure are obscured in the mature plant. Furthermore, having an open type of growth because of the persisting meristematic state of shoot and root tips and of the vascular cambium, the plant continuously adds new vascular tissues that are in dynamic relationship to one another. The role of the vascular tissues in the life of the plant cannot be properly understood unless they are studied developmentally in relation to the ontogeny of the whole plant; and conversely, the development of the vascular plant cannot be discussed comprehensively without reference to the differentiation of the vascular system. It is not surprising, therefore, that the topic of vascular differentiation is of such great interest to students of morphogenesis.

This book discusses the differentiation of the primary vascular tissues. The establishment of the primary vascular system is one of the fundamental aspects of organization of the plant body. The differentiation of the secondary vascular tissues, a rich topic in itself, is less involved in the establishment of the basic organization of the plant. As a background for the discussion of the primary vascular differentiation, the salient concepts of vascular organization and

v

structure of the primary vascular system are reviewed in the first two chapters. The chapters on differentiation deal with normally developing plants and with those treated experimentally in connection with studies of morphogenesis. A comparison of the discussions in this book with my earlier reviews on vascular differentiation (*The Botanical Review*, **9**: 125–26, 1943; *Biological Reviews*, **29**: 46–86, 1954) clearly shows the increasing emphasis on experimental approach to the solution of problems of vascularization. But much is still left to be done in a descriptive way on naturally developing plants. We do not yet have a full comprehension of the extent to which the phenomena of vascularization may vary in relation to the type and age of plant.

The present review emphasizes the literature published during the last ten years, but a considerable number of older references also are considered. Readers interested in a more comprehensive treatment of the older literature may want to study my 1943 review in *The Botanical Review*. The references are assembled at the end of the text because the various chapters are closely interrelated and some articles are used in more than one chapter.

The book is written for the advanced student and for the research worker. It discusses the subject critically and indicates areas that merit comprehensive investigation. Dr. V. I. Cheadle and Mr. C. L. Calvin helpfully reviewed the manuscript.

K.E.

Santa Barbara, California
April, 1965

contents

VASCULAR DIFFERENTIATION IN PLANTS

chapter one

Concepts of Vascular Organization

INTRODUCTION

The sporophyte of the vascular plant is characterized by a high degree of evolutionary specialization. Its vegetative body is typically differentiated into stem, leaf, and root and possesses an elaborate vascular system. Two kinds of conducting tissue are represented in this system; the xylem, concerned with conduction of water and substances dissolved in it; and the phloem, serving as a conduit for organic food materials. The conducting cells in the xylem are referred to as tracheary elements, and therefore the vascular plants are frequently classified as Tracheophyta. The gametophytes of Tracheophyta are generally devoid of vascular tissue, although those of *Psilotum* and certain ferns may contain some weakly developed tracheary tissue (Foster and Gifford, 1959).

The evolution of the vascular plant is thought to be associated with the transition from the aquatic to the terrestrial habitat (Bailey, 1953; Huber, 1956). The successful establishment of the land flora was largely dependent on the development of a water-conducting system. The process of obtaining carbon dioxide directly from the air through the stomata was correlated with a transpirational loss of water. The water, no longer bathing the entire surface of the plant, had to be moved from the soil to the photosynthesizing surfaces, a function eventually taken over by a new type of cell, the tracheary cell. The evolution of this cell involved elongation, increase in rigidity by development of thick lignified walls, and death of protoplasts. In the most highly evolved tracheary elements, parts of the walls, usually those at the two opposite ends, are removed during ontogeny. The end-to-end association of the open cells produces long tubes, the vessels, through which water can move freely.

1

In migration to land, plants ceased to be supported by surrounding water; tracheary cells became the stiffening structures. Specialized supporting cells, the fibers, appeared with further progress of evolution.

The evolution of the phloem is less well understood than that of the xylem, partly because the tissue is poorly preserved in fossils, partly because its study is technically difficult. In Tracheophyta the phloem is typically associated with the xylem, and the two tissues arise from the same meristem. The morphologic evolutionary changes in the two tissues, such as length and width of cells and their arrangement, were synchronized to a high degree because they occurred primarily in the meristems from which the tissues developed. But the principal conducting cell, the sieve element, assumed distinctive characteristics. Its protoplast did not disappear but became considerably modified, and a high degree of intercellular continuity was established through the sieve areas in the walls. The cell became adapted to rapid longitudinal conduction of organic materials. The task of conducting photosynthates is faced by water plants as well as by land plants, and indeed, some algae have developed a phloem tissue resembling that of the angiosperms (Esau et al., 1953).

ONTOGENETIC STAGES OF THE VASCULAR SYSTEM

When viewed broadly, two stages may be discerned in vascular differentiation. The first or primary stage encompasses the initiation and development of the vascular system in the embryo, the seedling, and shoot and root parts produced by the apical meristems. This stage coincides with the primary-growth stage of the plant as a whole. Primary growth culminates in reproductive structures, including flowers, fruits, and seeds in the higher Tracheophyta. Lower vascular plants and monocotyledons generally form their entire plant body by primary growth, whereas gymnosperms and dicotyledons undergo secondary growth after completing the primary. During secondary growth the amount of vascular tissues of root and shoot is augmented by the activity of a localized meristem, the vascular cambium. This growth causes an increase in thickness of root and shoot axes and provides conducting and supporting tissues for the branching and enlarging body, as illustrated by a shrub or a tree.

The secondary tissues are added in successive growth increments, and each is continuous with the primary vascular tissues formed during the same growth period. Thus the movement of water from the root to the leaf, and the translocation of food from the photosynthesizing leaf to the food-utilizing shoot and root parts, occur through conduits that are continuous, across the latest additions of secondary tissues, from the youngest primary vascular tissue in the shoot to that of the root.

THE VASCULAR SYSTEM AND THE STELE

The vascular tissue forms a continuous system extending from near the tips of roots to vein endings in leaves, as well as to floral parts, fruits, and seeds if these are present. In higher plants having no secondary growth and in the younger, primary, parts of plants having secondary growth, the vascular system of the aerial plant body consists of more or less distinct strands interconnected with each other in various patterns. The primary vascular system of the root and of the entire axis in some of the lower vascular plants is rather compact. With some exceptions, the secondary vascular tissues form a solid body.

The vascular system is imbedded in nonvascular tissue commonly referred to as ground tissue. This tissue may be composed of different kinds of cells, each frequently forming a more or less solid complex, as, for example, collenchyma or sclerenchyma in the outer cortex, parenchyma in the inner cortex, photosynthetic parenchyma in the leaf, and parenchyma, sclerenchyma, or both in the pith. The vascular tissues are commonly surrounded by parenchyma and are associated with sclerenchyma. A considerable proportion of sclerenchyma arises from the same meristem as the vascular tissues do and is therefore treated as part of the vascular system.

The recognition of unity of the vascular system has led to the development of the concept of the stele first formulated by Van Tieghem (Van Tieghem and Douliot, 1886). The stele was originally defined as a column occupying the center of the axis, the central cylinder, and composed of vascular tissues and the associated ground tissue—pith, medullary rays (that is, tissue between the vascular bundles), and the peripherally located pericycle. At present, many authors use the word "stele" to designate only the vascular system. Van Tieghem discussed the variability in the relation between the vascular and the ground tissue of the stele and proposed a classification of steles on the basis of this variability (see Foster and Gifford, 1959). Thus he developed the stelar concept into the stelar theory.

Van Tieghem's emphasis on the morphologic importance of the vascular cylinder as a whole resulted in a considerable advance in the understanding of comparative structure of vascular plants and stimulated active research on the vascular system as such. Many morphologists adopted the stelar concept and used it extensively in comparative studies of plants, especially the ferns. Others, however, found the concept irreconcilable with their understanding of plant structure. The two principal subjects of intensive debate with regard to the validity of the stelar theory were (1) the cell layers delimiting the stele from the cortex and (2) the relation of the vascular supply of the leaves to the stele.

Delimitation of the stele

According to Van Tieghem (1882), the limits between the cortex and the stele are given by the innermost cortical layer (or layers), the endodermis, and by the outermost region of the stele, the pericycle. (In lower plants the endodermis and pericycle may originate from the same meristematic layer; Ogura, 1938.) In this view, the pericycle constitutes part of the ground tissue of the stele (the "conjonctif" of Van Tieghem) and contains parenchyma, sclerenchyma, or both types of tissue. The followers of Van Tieghem surveyed many plants with regard to the outer region of the central cylinder and concluded that a pericycle was generally present in the axes of vascular plants (see Esau, 1943c). This interpretation, however, was opposed by some authors on the basis of ontogenetic considerations. Léger (1897), for example, provided evidence that with some exceptions, the region called pericycle in stems of higher plants develops from the outermost, or earliest, part of the phloem. As the stem ages, the first sieve elements cease to function and are obliterated, whereas the remaining cells elongate, and increase in width; in many species, they differentiate into fibers. The phloic origin of the so-called pericycle in stems of seed plants has been confirmed by many other authors since Léger (see Blyth, 1958; Esau, 1950). Even one of the outstanding contributors to the development of the stelar theory, Brebner (1902), pointed out the questionable value of the concept of pericycle because of the variable origin of the tissue region so named. Another important proponent of the stelar theory, Schoute (1903), agreed that this theory cannot be defended on the basis of ontogenetic data, but insisted that in more advanced stages of development a sufficiently distinct limiting layer occurs between the cortex and the vascular cylinder to make the stelar theory valid.

The morphological distinctness of the endodermis varies in different groups of plants and in different parts of the same plant, but histochemically it is detectable. According to the studies of Van Fleet (1961), the boundary between the vascular and nonvascular tissues has distinctive histochemical properties that change during the development of the plant organ and are related to the interaction between substances originating in two biochemically distinct regions, vascular and nonvascular. Histochemically, the endodermis thus gives a topographic and physiologic delimitation of the vascular region throughout the plant, but in the sense of a typical morphologic terminology it can hardly be considered a limiting layer as required by the stelar theory.

Axes with more clearly delimited vascular region (roots, stems of lower vascular plants) commonly have a morphologically distinct endodermis characterized by special wall characteristics. Such axes also have a more or less wide tissue region between the endodermis and the most peripheral vascular elements. If the term "pericycle" is to be maintained, it is applicable to this region. In the stems of the majority of seed plants investigated developmentally, the endodermis is not definable on the basis of wall characteristics—it is sometimes differentiated as a starch sheath, however—and the phloem differentiates in contact with the cortex. Thus, in such stems the pericycle, in the sense of a tissue distinct from the vascular (the "conjonctif" of Van Tieghem), is absent.

The stele and the leaf traces

The second problem posed by the stelar concept—the relation of the stele to the vascular supply of the leaves—has been formulated as a result of the common observation that in the ferns and the seed plants the vascular system of the stem is connected with the leaves in such a way that it seems to consist partly or entirely of vascular bundles pertaining to the leaves. At a given node, one or more vascular bundles—the so-called leaf traces—bend away from the vascular system of the stem and extend into the leaf, where the vascular system permeates the mesophyll in one or another characteristic venation pattern. If followed downward, the leaf trace may be found continuing through several nodes and internodes before it is connected with another bundle of the vascular system. In ferns and seed plants these other bundles are also commonly related to leaves; they may be leaf traces or complexes of leaf traces in the sense that at higher levels more than one leaf trace diverges from them into the leaves. It is convenient to call the trace complexes sympodia of leaf traces.

The introduction of the leaf-trace concept (Hanstein, 1858) preceded that of the stelar concept, and some morphologists found the two concepts irreconcilable. According to Campbell (1921; see also Nozu, 1956), for example, the young sporophyte of an ophioglossaceous fern consists only of a leaf and a root with the vascular strand continuous between the two. In the older sporophyte the vascular system of the axis is built up of leaf traces to which the bundles of roots are joined. Thus, Campbell posed the question whether the stem under consideration had its own, cauline, vascular tissue, or whether all its vascular tissue was foliar in origin. The view of Bower (1923, 1926) was that cauline tissue does exist in the stem but its amount varies in relation to the proportionate size of stem and leaf. In ferns the leaf is dominant and the stele is composed of leaf traces to a large extent. In lycopods the stem predominates and the greater part of the stele is cauline.

The treatment of the relationship between stele and leaf trace affects the interpretation of the nature of the parenchyma accompanying the vascular tissue in the stele. According to the stelar theory, the vascular system of the stem is phylogenetically derived from a more or less compact vascular column which through parenchymatization became divided into strands. Thus the parenchyma of the stele is potentially vascular tissue (Boodle, 1903; Wardlaw, 1952). If, on the other hand, the vascular system is interpreted as a composite of leaf traces, the apparent breaks in the continuity of the vascular system are simply spaces among the coalescent leaf traces, and the pith is ground tissue included within the network of bundles (Campbell, 1921).

The concept of the leaf trace in relation to the stele has a parallel in the growth-unit or phytonic concept with regard to the shoot as a whole. According to the phytonic concept, the shoot consists of phytons (or phyllomes, Cuénod, 1951), each composed of one leaf and the subjacent stem segment (Mitra and Majumdar, 1952; Wetmore, 1943). This hypothetical growth unit has no exact boundaries (e.g., Galinat, 1959). In relating the vascular organization to the phytonic concept, Priestley, Scott, and Gillett (1935) describe the unit of shoot growth as the segment of the axis that subtends a leaf initial and surrounds its leaf trace. Since a leaf trace extends through more than one internode, the growth unit in this conception likewise must extend through more than one internode. The delimitation of such a growth unit would be extremely indefinite, especially if the leaf had more than one trace.

On evolution of the leaf

The conflicting views on the structure of the vascular system of the shoot cannot be resolved without reference to the evolution of the leafy shoot. According to a prevalent view, the early vascular plants were leafless axes not differentiated into stem and root (Foster and Gifford, 1959). The steps in the evolutionary divergence of the roots are quite obscure, but the evolutionary history of the leaves is usually interpreted on the basis of definite assumptions. The prototypes of leaves of Pteropsida (ferns and seed plants) are thought to be aerial branches. Evolution of leaves from branches began with a change from the original equal dichotomous branching to an unequal development of the two member branches of the dichotomy, the larger of which would continue as the main axis and thus "overtop" the smaller. The subdivisions of the overtopped branch underwent flattening (Fig. 1-1, A and B) and subsequently fusion and webbing. Thus, the branch assumed an expanded form —it became a leaf—clearly distinct from the cylindrical central axis; and the former branch traces (e.g., Fig. 1-1, C–E) became leaf traces.

Thus a cladogenous evolutionary origin, that is, origin from a branch, or clados, is visualized with reference to the leaves of Pteropsida. The relatively small leaves with weakly developed leaf traces in Lycopsida (*Lycopodium* and *Selaginella*) and in certain

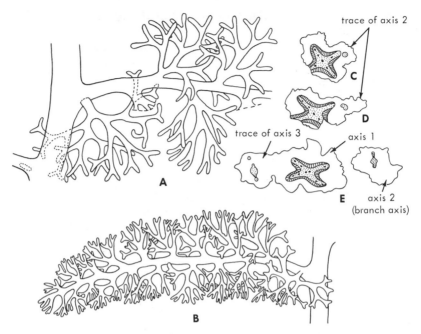

Fig. 1–1. Precursors of leaves and leaf traces. (*A* and *B*) Ancient "leaves": reconstitution of vegetative pinna (*B*) and several pinnules (*A*) of *Racophyton zygopteroides*. The pinnules are dichotomously branched. (*C–E*) Three levels of axis of *Tetraxylopteris schmidtii* in cross sections. The trace of a branch axis diverges from one of the four xylem ridges in the parent axis (*C*). Protoxylem black, metaxylem stippled, secondary xylem hatched. (*A, B,* after Leclerq [1951]; *C–E,* after Beck [1957].)

other lower plants (Foster and Gifford, 1959) are frequently interpreted as superficial lateral outgrowths (enations) from the naked stems of primitive vascular plants. This type of leaf is called microphyll whereas the cladogenous leaf is called megaphyll.

The existence of a fundamental distinction between microphylls and megaphylls is questioned by some authors (e.g., Martens, 1950; Wardlaw, 1957) but the theory of the origin of the leaf from a branch or a branch system in Pteropsida continues to be regarded as valid (e.g., Andrews, 1961; Beck, 1957; Foster and Gifford, 1959). Evolution of the leaf from a branch would signify that the vascular strands of stem and leaf were primitively identical structures (Tansley, 1907–1908). In the dichotomously branched ancient plant, the vascular system was repeatedly divided into equivalent branch traces. In the leafy shoot of a megaphyllous plant, however, the branching of the vascular system is no longer equivalent, since the leaf trace is smaller than the portion of vascular system from which it diverges in the stem; and in the microphyllous plant the leaf trace is only a minor part of the axial vascular system.

CONCLUSION

The vascular tissues of a plant are organized into a morphologically and physiologically unified system in which the parts are as harmoniously related to one another as are the parts of the plant itself. Thus, the vascular system reflects the structural organization of the plant and can be analyzed on the basis of this parallelism. The concept of the stele emphasizes the unity of the vascular system of the axis, whereas the concept of the leaf trace stresses the relation between the axial and the foliar vascular systems. The two concepts do not conflict with one another if that of the leaf trace is put in proper perspective. A leaf trace does not "belong" to a leaf exclusively. Topographically, leaf traces are axial or cauline parts of the vascular system of the shoot; but their existence, arrangement, ontogeny, and mature characteristics are determined by the association of the stem with the leaves. In the megaphyllous plant the leaf plays a more important role in shaping the vascular system of the stem than in the microphyllous plant. The concept that leaf traces and cauline vascular tissue are morphologically distinct is highly artificial.

chapter two

Vascular System and Phyllotaxis

THE DEVELOPMENTAL APPROACH TO THE STUDY OF VASCULAR ORGANIZATION

Plant scientists are much concerned with the causal factors in the development of the specific form of the plant (morphogenesis), external and internal. The ontogeny of the sporophyte plant from a fertilized egg is an orderly sequence of events resulting in a definite grouping and arrangement of parts and in an establishment of specific mutual relationships among them. In other words, the structure of the plant assumes a specific pattern; the plant is an organized entity. The vascular system reflects the organization of the plant, and therefore its development is of interest to investigators concerned with problems of morphogenesis. Some workers study vascular differentiation as it occurs during the normal development of the plant; others seek to uncover the causal relations in this differentiation by treating the plant in various ways and relating the resulting developmental changes to normal phenomena.

The origin of procambium, the meristem that forms the primary vascular tissues, is of special interest among the many specific aspects of vascular differentiation. This beginning stage of vascularization reflects the intrinsic organizational differences between the root and the shoot, one a purely axial organ, the other a more complex organ differentiated into axis and leaves. Procambial origin is investigated in embryos, in roots, in vegetative and reproductive shoots, and in the especially problematic transition region, through which the root and the shoot are connected.

One of the much debated questions is whether the procambium, as it is first organized in new increments of the shoot, is independent of the vascular tissue in the stem below or whether it differentiates progressively from older parts of the shoot toward the newer. Stated in another way, the question is whether in the shoot the procambium differentiates basipetally (away from the apex) or acropetally (toward the apex).

The pattern of differentiation of the primary phloem and xylem in the root, the shoot, and the transition region is another important topic for study. This pattern, like that of procambial development, mirrors the difference between the root and the shoot and serves for discussions of the physiologic aspects of vascularization of newly formed parts of the two organs.

Studies on the initial vascularization bear directly on the question of the morphologic relation between leaf and stem and on the classic concept of the stele. The interrelationships of plant organs, tissues, and tissue regions are difficult to assess after their development is completed. Studies on the ontogeny of the vascular system have made major contributions toward interpretation of organizational relationships in the plant.

The phyllotaxis, or the arrangement of leaves on the shoot, is one of the expressions of organization of the plant. Numbers of leaf-trace sympodia, numerical relations in the interconnections of leaf traces in the sympodia, and sequences of differentiation of xylem and phloem in the leaves and their traces are related to phyllotaxis. A discussion of phyllotaxis is an essential part of a review on differentiation of the vascular system in the shoot.

PHYLLOTAXIS

Leaf arrangement varies in different plants, but whatever this arrangement, a high degree of regularity characterizes the phenomenon. The majority of phyllotactic patterns are based on spiral (helical) arrangement of leaves (see Sinnott, 1960, pp. 150-159). The single spiral that can be drawn through the centers of all the leaves in the order of their succession is called the ontogenetic or genetic spiral (Fig. 2-1, C). This spiral was used by the early botanists to determine the numerical value of phyllotaxis. They expressed the phyllotaxis by a fraction in which the numerator is the number of windings of the genetic spiral and the denominator the number of leaves intervening between two vertically superimposed leaves. In Figure 2-1, C, for example, the phyllotaxis thus calculated

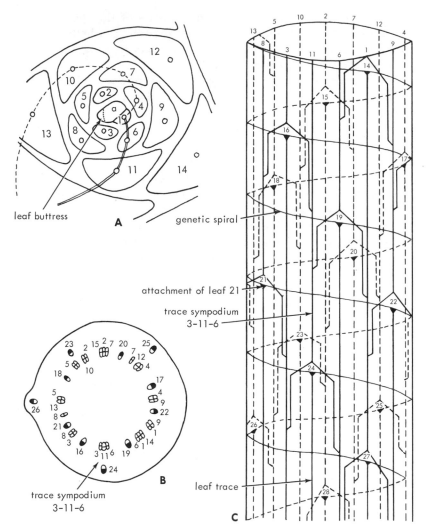

leaf buttress

A

genetic spiral

attachment of leaf 21

trace sympodium
3-11-6

trace sympodium
3-11-6

B

leaf trace

C

Fig. 2–1. Diagrams of the primary vascular system of *Hectorella caespitosa* in transections (*A* and *B*) and in three-dimensional view (*C*). (*A*) Stem apex (*a*) and leaves 1 to 14, in each of which the midrib is indicated by a circle. The buttress to a new leaf primordium is separated by a dotted line from *a*. The two curved lines (one broken, the other double) indicate a pair of contact parastichies. (*B*) Stem cut near node of leaf 23. The traces cut above the level of their connections with other traces are indicated by blackened phloem regions. (*C*) Diagram showing interconnections of leaf traces. (After Skipworth [1962].)

12

would be $\frac{5}{13}$ (see attachment of leaves 14 and 27 or 15 and 28). The common fractions are $\frac{1}{2}$, $\frac{1}{3}$, $\frac{2}{5}$, $\frac{3}{8}$, the less common ones $\frac{5}{13}$, $\frac{8}{21}$, and higher. This series of fractions belongs to the so-called Fibonacci summation series 0, 1, 1, 2, 3, 5, 8, 13, 21. . . . The numerator and denominator of each succeeding fraction is the sum of the numerators and denominators of the two preceding fractions. Each of these fractions represents the angle (fraction of the circumference) intervening between the centers of two successive leaf primordia. This angle is approximately 137.5 for all fractions. Dormer (1955b) suggests, therefore, that with some few exceptions all genetic spirals are probably alike.

The fractional characterization of phyllotaxis was usually made by examination of mature shoots in which one can find approximately superimposed leaves, that is, leaves arranged along straight lines, or orthostichies (Fig. 2-1, C). If, however, leaf arrangement is studied at the apex, that is, in the place of origin of leaves, no straight-line relationship is discernible in shoots with alternately inserted leaves; the apparently superimposed leaves occur along steep spirals (Loiseau, 1959). Slight secondary torsions occur in the stem during growth and effect a straight-line relationship within certain leaf series (Snow and Snow, 1934). Presently, students of phyllotaxis refer only to spiral sequences, or parastichies, in their discussions of leaf arrangement in shoots with alternately placed leaves (see Sinnott, 1960). Spirality is characteristic also of the arrangement of sporophylls—anthotaxis—and of semaphylls, that is, petals, sepals, and bracts—semataxis (Leppik, 1961).

Numerous parastichies can be recognized in a given shoot, some winding clockwise, others counterclockwise. Along certain of these parastichies the leaves of seed plants are proximal to one another when they are initiated at the apex, that is, before the internodes elongate. These parastichies are called contact parastichies (Church, 1904; Snow, 1955). Usually two sets of contact parastichies are recognized, the members of one set winding in a direction opposite to that of the other. The common numbers of such parastichies are 2 + 3, 3 + 5 (Fig. 2-2, A and B), and 5 + 8 (Fig. 2-2, D and E), again numbers belonging to the Fibonacci series. Sometimes the contact parastichy sets follow the subsidiary Fibonacci series, 1, 3, 4, 7, 11 . . . (Fig. 2-3, A and B; 4 + 7 contact parastichies). In some plants three sets of contact parastichies are discernible (Fig. 2-1, A;

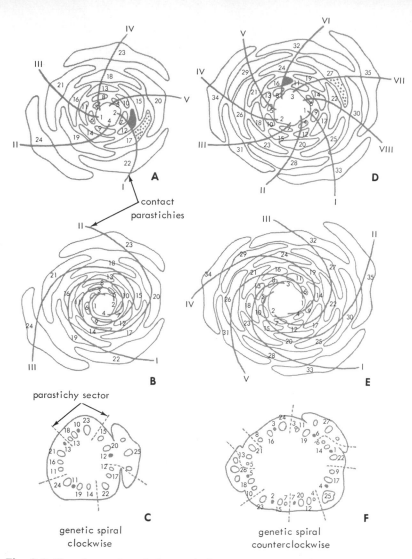

Fig. 2–2. Vasculature in relation to leaf arrangement in *Linum usitatissimum* (flax). Transverse sections. Two shoots, each represented by three drawings. The members in each of the pairs of drawings *A* and *B* and *D* and *E* are identical, except for the indications of parastichies. One shoot (*A–C*) has five parastichy sectors in the stem (*C*) and leaves arranged in 3 + 5 contact parastichies. The other shoot (*D–F*) has eight parastichy sectors in the stem (*F*) and leaves arranged in 5 + 8 contact parastichies. Leaf traces in a parastichy sector, indicated by open ovals, have primary connections with one another. The bundles shown in black are half-traces from adjacent parastichy sectors. Leaves with first mature sieve tubes are half-blackened in *A* and *D*; leaves with first mature xylem elements are half-stippled in *A* and *D*. (Adapted from Girolami [1953].)

14

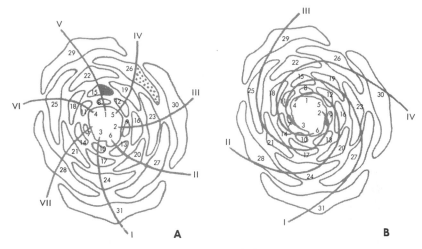

genetic spiral counterclockwise

A   B

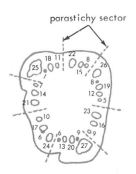

parastichy sector

C

Fig. 2–3. Vasculature in relation to leaf arrangement in *Linum usitatissimum* (flax). Transverse sections. (*A* and *B*) Two views of same section cut near the apex and showing the disposition of leaves. They form $4+7$ contact parastichies. (*C*) Stem with seven parastichy sectors marked off by dashed lines. Blackened bundles are half-traces from adjacent parastichy sectors. Leaf with first mature sieve tube is half-blackened and leaf with first mature xylem element is half-stippled in *A*. (Adapted from Girolami [1953].)

the two that are indicated by one parastichy in each and a third with parastichies passing through leaves 1, 3, 5, 7, 9, 11 . . . and 2, 4, 6, 8, 10, 12. . .).

The phyllotaxis is simpler in plants with a decussate leaf arrangement, that is, with two leaves opposite one another at each node, but the pair at one node rotated at 90° to that at the next node (Fig. 2-4). Such plants have four rows or orthostichies of leaves and one set of two contact parastichies. Plants with two-ranked leaf arrangement—one leaf per node, with the leaves at successive nodes located at opposite sides—have two orthostichies and a single parastichy, a helix which is equivalent to the genetic spiral (for example, grasses).

In plants with alternately arranged leaves, the differences in phyllotactic values (fractions or numbers of contact parastichies) depend on the size of the apical meristem or, more precisely, on the relation between the size of the emerging leaf primordium (leaf buttress in Fig. 2-1, A) and that of the apical meristem not involved in leaf formation at that time (area a in Fig 2-1, A). When the apical-meristem area is relatively large, the phyllotactic value is higher. In Figure 2-2, for example, the shoot in D and E has a larger apical area and a larger number of contact parastichies than the shoot in A and B.

During the development of a vegetative plant from a seedling, its leaf arrangement commonly changes from lower to higher phyllotactic values. This change is referable to the increase in size of the apex in relation to the size of the leaf buttress (Gifford and Tepper, 1962; Richards, 1948). Further increase in the phyllotactic value may occur at the onset of the reproductive stage. In the pineapple, for example, the apex broadens notably at transition from initiation of leaves to that of floral bracts, and the phyllotaxis shifts from $\frac{5}{13}$ to $\frac{8}{21}$ (Kerns, Collins, and Kim, 1936). Later, during the formation of the crown above the inflorescence, the apex again diminishes in size and the phyllotaxis drops to $\frac{5}{13}$. Millener (1952) obtained a change to higher systems of phyllotaxis by increasing the rate of growth—and presumably also the size of the apex—in *Ulex europaeus* treated with various combinations of light and temperature. Main and lateral shoots may differ in phyllotaxis, sometimes very conspicuously (Tucker, 1962).

PHYLLOTAXIS AND THE PLASTOCHRON

Since phyllotaxis is a developmental phenomenon, the basic developmental concept of plastochron applicable to shoot growth is used in discussions on phyllotaxis. Plastochron refers to the time interval between two of a series of similar events, or a phase in the periodic phenomenon of organ formation. The events may be initiations of leaf primordia, attainment of certain size by leaf primordia or certain length by internodes, or other periodic growth phenomena. The concept of the plastochron has been used in the establishment of the plastochron index for developmental studies (see Erickson, 1959). With regard to chronological time, developmental phenomena proceed at highly varied rates, but with regard to the age of the leaf expressed in plastochrons, the relative rate of change in such values as dry weight, chlorophyll synthesis, and oxygen uptake of individual leaves is remarkably consistent (Michelini, 1958).

The development of leaves in *Kalanchoë* (Stein and Stein, 1960) may be used to illustrate the concept of plastochron. Figure 2-4 shows the shoot of this plant in transection. The phyllotaxis is decussate, so that one plastochron refers to the development of a pair of leaves, rather than a single leaf, and its starting point is here considered to be the initiation of a pair. The leaves were numbered beginning with the first pair above the cotyledons. The plant in Figure 2-4 was in its eighth plastochron; that is, the eighth pair of leaves was initiated.

The diameter of a shoot apex along which a new pair of leaves arises attains its maximum length just before the primordia are initiated. This is the maximal stage of development of the apex as seen along that particular diameter. Figure 2-5, A, illustrates the maximal stage for the shoot apex of *Kalanchoë* before the leaves of pair 8 emerged as visible primordia. Four stages in the development of this pair of leaves are shown in Figures 2-5, B and C, and Figures 2-6 and 2-7. Plastochron 8 was completed at the stage depicted in Figure 2-6 because in the subsequent stage (Fig. 2-7) leaf pair 9 was initiated. In *Kalanchoë* the shoot tip grows with sufficient regularity so that the plastochronic stage can be predicted without dissecting the shoot apex (Stein and Stein, 1960). A new leaf $x + 1$ is produced when leaf x is 0.4 mm long, $x + 2$ when x is 6.6 mm long.

In applying the concept of plastochron to phyllotactic phenomena, one can say, by reference to *Hectorella* (Skipworth, 1962), for example, that leaves approximately superimposed are 13 plastochrons apart (Fig. 2-1, C, leaves 14 and 27); and in the three contact parastichies (Fig. 2-1, A) the plastochronic intervals are 2 (leaves 1, 3, 5, etc.), 3 (leaves 1, 4, 7, etc.), and 5 (leaves 1, 6, 11, etc.). Van Iterson (1907) used the value of plastochronic intervals between the primordia within contact parastichies for characterizing the phyllotaxis of a given shoot. The values are the same as those obtained when

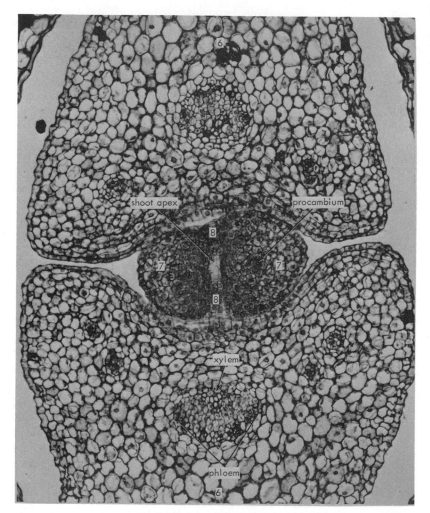

Fig. 2-4. Transection of shoot tip of *Kalanchoë* in early plastochron 8. Primordia of leaf pair 8 had just been initiated. The light area between them is the outer cell layer of the apex. Compare with Figure 2–5, *B*. × 200. (From Stein and Stein [1960]; courtesy of Brookhaven National Laboratory.)

the contact parastichies as such are counted. (See Figs. 2-2 and 2-3.) Richards (1948, 1956) employed the plastochron ratio—the ratio between the distances of centers of two successive leaf primordia

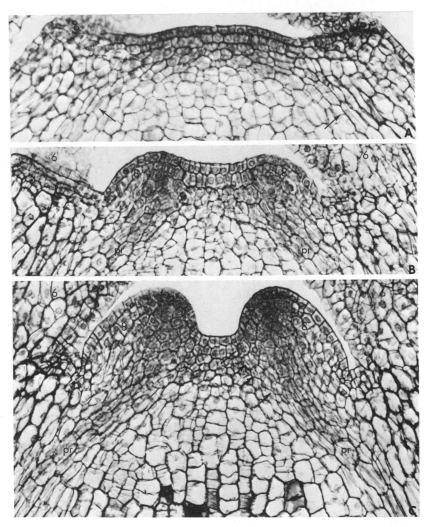

Fig. 2–5. Form changes of shoot tip of *Kalanchoë* during one plastochron. Longitudinal sections. (*A*) End of plastochron 7; apex in maximal stage. (*B*) Early plastochron 8; leaf pair 8 has been initiated; each leaf has procambium (*pr*). (*C*) Mid-stage of plastochron 8. Lengths of leaves: (*A*) leaf 7 (not shown) 0.39 mm; leaf 8, 0.0 mm; (*B*) leaf 7, 1.0 mm; leaf 8, 0.06 mm; (*C*) leaf 7, 1.5 mm; leaf 8, 0.1 mm. Unlabeled arrows in (*A*) and (*C*) mark elongated cells that do not constitute part of procambium. They are concerned with growth in the leaf axil. All × 236. (From Stein and Stein [1960]; courtesy of Brookhaven National Laboratory.)

19

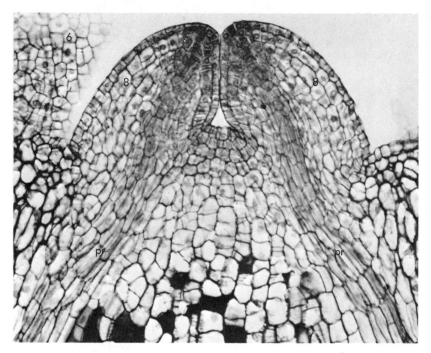

Fig. 2–6. Longitudinal section of shoot tip of *Kalanchoë* in late plastochron 8. Apex in minimal stage. Lengths of leaves: leaf 7 (not shown), 3.0 mm; leaf 8, 0.18 mm. Procambium at *pr*. × 235. (From Stein and Stein [1960]; courtesy of Brookhaven National Laboratory.)

from the center of the shoot apex—for characterizing the phyllotaxis.

The developmental change in phyllotaxis expressed in plastochron ratios is illustrated by Gifford and Tepper (1962). In *Chenopodium album* the plastochron ratio changed from 1.087 to 1.046 through several stages of vegetative development. Concomitantly the contact parastichy numbers increased from 2 + 3 to 3 + 5, an indication of increase in the size of the apex. A change in the rate of leaf production was also observed; in other words, a change in phyllotaxis was associated with a change in the duration of the plastochron.

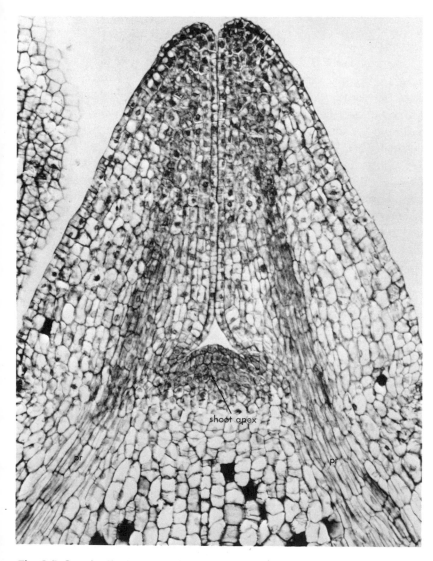

Fig. 2–7. Longitudinal section of shoot tip of *Kalanchoë* in early plastochron 9. The pair of large leaf primordia are those of plastochron 8 (see Figs. 2–5 and 2–6). The primordia of pair 9 are in a plane perpendicular to that of pair 8. Lengths of leaves: leaf 7 (not shown), 6.6 mm; leaf 8, 0.4 mm. Procambium at *pr.* × 200. (From Stein and Stein [1960]; courtesy of Brookhaven National Laboratory.)

21

PRIMARY VASCULAR PATTERNS IN SEED PLANTS

As discussed before, the primary vascular system in shoots of most seed plants can be interpreted in terms of leaf traces and leaf-trace sympodia. (Some authors use the term "stem bundles" for the sympodia; see Dormer, 1954; Ezelarab and Dormer, 1963). Two basic types of leaf-trace interconnections occur in seed plants. In one the leaf traces diverge from a sympodium on one side only, so that the sympodia remain independent of one another (Figs. 2-8, A; 2-12). In the second type a leaf trace is related to more than one sympodium and thus the sympodia are interconnected with one another (Figs. 2-1, C; 2-8, B; 2-9, B). Dormer (1945, 1954) calls the two systems open and closed, respectively. In the older literature they were known as sympodial and reticulate (see Philipson and Balfour, 1963).

The literature on vascular organization uses the concept of leaf gap or lacuna in discussions of nodal anatomy. Leaf gap refers to the parenchymatic region opposite the leaf trace where the latter

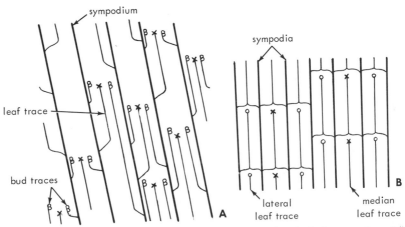

Fig. 2–8. Diagrams of vascular system (shown in one plane) of the open type (*A*) and closed type (*B*). Heavy lines, trace sympodia; crosses, median leaf traces; circles, lateral leaf traces; β, bud traces. *A, Mimosa Spegazzinii; B, Ornithopus sativus.* (After Dormer [1945].)

bends toward the leaf. In Figure 3-2, F, for example, a leaf gap occurs between traces 6 and 3, opposite leaf bundle 11. In Figure 2-2, F, a leaf gap appears in front of leaf trace 25; in Figure 2-3, C, in front of traces 25 and 27. In a closed type of system the gap is delimited above by the branching[1] of a sympodium of traces above a trace of a lower leaf (Fig. 2-1, C, trace sympodium 3-11-6 branches above attachment of leaf 24). In systems composed of bundles clearly separated from one another by interfascicular regions of parenchyma (medullary rays; Figs. 2-1, 2-2, and 2-3) the gaps are confluent with these regions on the sides of leaf insertions in closed systems (Figs. 2-1, C, and 2-8, B); and above the leaf insertions as well in open systems (Fig. 2-8, A). Thus, the delimitation of the leaf gap in the primary body is highly artificial, but the concept is used extensively in comparative studies of nodal anatomy (see Carlquist, 1961). During secondary growth the gaps become more clearly delimited because secondary vascular tissues appear in the interfascicular regions before they do so in the gap regions.

The occurrence of open and closed primary vascular systems possibly has physiological significance. Dormer (1945) suggests that the open system, in lacking tangential continuity, is relatively inefficient, but that such systems usually occur in plants in which secondary growth from the vascular cambium early establishes the necessary lateral continuity. In his studies he found no extreme herbs with open vascular systems.

The vascular supply of the branches, if such develop on a given shoot, is connected with the vascular system of the main stem in a manner resembling the connections of leaves. The branch traces, frequently two (Fig. 2-8, A), are leaf traces also: they furnish the vascular supply of the first leaves on the axillary shoot, that is, of the prophylls. Traces of one or more additional leaves may be prolonged in the main axis (Tucker, 1963).

According to Dormer (1955a), the extent of the connection of an axillary bud with the main axis depends on the degree of development of the bud. In *Asarum* (Fig. 2-9), for example, the bud that remains dormant is connected with only two leaf-trace sympodia in the stem (Fig. 2-9, C), whereas the vigorous bud that continues the

---

[1] The words "branching" and "connection" have no developmental significance in this discussion; they refer only to the topographic aspects.

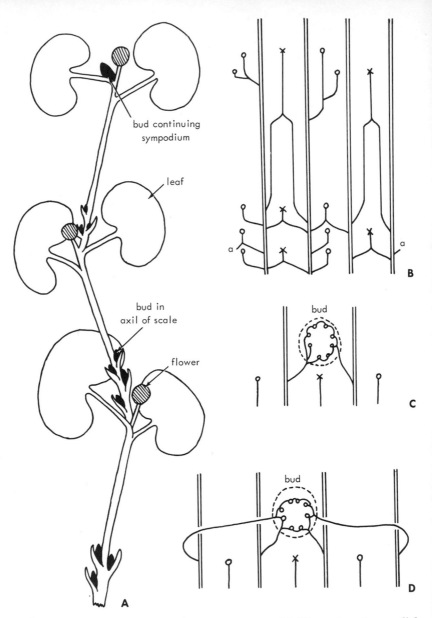

Fig. 2-9. Vasculature of shoot of *Asarum europaeum*. (*A*) Illustration of sympodial structure of shoot. (*B*) Vascular system of lower part of shoot in *A* spread in one plane. At *a* are two parts of same bundle. (*C*) Vascular supply to bud in axil of scale leaf. (*D*) Vascular supply to large bud that continues the shoot sympodium. In *B–D*, double lines show sympodia of leaf traces; crosses, median leaf traces; circles (in main axis) lateral leaf traces. In *B*, three lower crosses indicate median traces of three scale leaves; bud traces are omitted. (After Dormer [1955a].)

24

shoot sympodium (Fig. 2-9, A) is connected with four leaf-trace sympodia (Fig. 2-9, D).

The number of leaf traces per leaf varies in different species. The vascular systems with a single trace to a leaf are simpler in structure than those with several traces to a leaf; and at lower levels of shoots where the phyllotaxis changes rapidly during development (starting with opposite leaves and shifting to spiral arrangement), the trace interconnections may be rather irregular.

The trace relationships are highly complex in shoots whose leaves have numerous traces. Figure 2-10 illustrates such a system for *Zea* (Kumazawa, 1961). The leaves are in a two-ranked arrangement so that the median traces (*m*) of successive leaves appear on alternate sides (Fig. 2-10, A). Characteristically, median bundles and larger lateral bundles appear closer to the center of the stem in parts of their course, usually the upper, and closer to the periphery in other parts; the most peripheral bundles are not connected with others except at the lowermost level of the stem. If one disregards this connection, the peripheral system appears completely independent from the inner. Figures 2-10, B and C, illustrate these two systems separately and show their connection with an axillary shoot. Two independent systems have been observed also in the pistillate inflorescence, the maize ear (Laubengayer, 1949). In Figure 2-11, A, these two systems appear together, in Figure 2-11, B and C, separately, as they were dissected out of a macerated maize ear.

These examples should suffice to indicate the variability and complexity of the primary vascular system. Developmental studies of these systems cannot be carried out successfully without a complete knowledge of the mature system and its relation to the leaves. For this reason, most of the developmental studies have been made on relatively simple systems, those with one or three traces per leaf.

PHYLLOTAXIS AND LEAF-TRACE CONNECTIONS

The leaf traces in a seed plant commonly have numerical relations with one another that are similar to those revealed in the phyllotactic patterns of leaves. These relations are particularly obvious in systems in which each leaf has a single trace and the trace sympodia are not interconnected into a reticulum (open systems). Figure 2-12 compares the leaf arrangement with the connec-

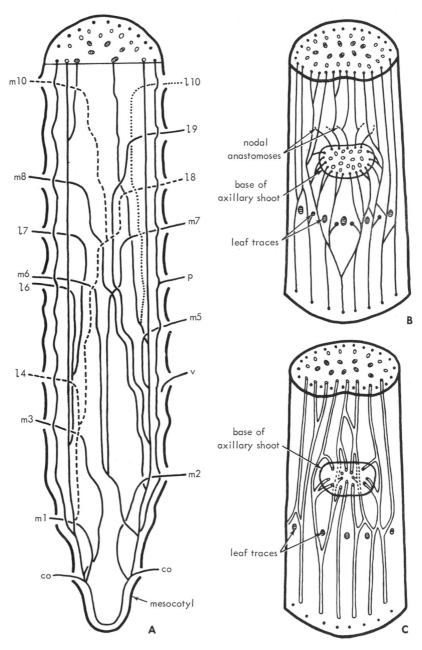

Fig. 2-10.

tions of leaf traces into sympodia in a *Sequoia* shoot. In the two contact parastichies indicated in Figure 2-12, A, the plastochronic intervals between two successive leaves in the same parastichy are 3 and 5. The traces are united not along these parastichies but along those with a plastochronic interval of 13 (Fig. 2-12, B). These parastichies are considerably steeper than the contact parastichies. The number of windings of the genetic spiral between two leaves whose traces are interconnected (for example, leaves 1 and 14) is 5. Again we have a series of numbers, 3, 5, and 13, that belong to the Fibonacci summation series.

In contrast to the *Sequoia* shoot, that of *Hectorella* (Fig. 2-1) has a closed vascular system since the leaf traces are doubly inter-connected. As seen in Figure 2-1, C, one connection is based on the plastochronic interval of 5 (for example, leaves 1-6-11-16), the other on the interval of 8 (3-11-19-27). According to Skipworth (1962), the continuity of traces at the interval of 5 is present earlier (primary connection) in the ontogeny of the shoot than is the continuity at the interval of 8 (secondary connection). Thus, for a time, the system is an open one. In this example, the merging of two halves of a sympodium (or branching, when followed in down-ward direction) occurs above a leaf that is 13 plastochrons removed from the leaf whose trace is the oldest component of the branching sympodium (for example, 9 over 22). One can say that the sym-podium containing trace 9 branches above the gap of leaf 22. These numerical relations are further elucidated in the cross section in Figure 2-1, B, in which the trace sympodia are shown with the component traces delimited individually for clarity; in the plant, the traces composing sympodia are commonly confluent. Trace 23 (Fig. 2-1, B) appears opposite the gap formed by the branching of sympodium 5-10-2, in which 10 is the oldest trace. The secondary connection of trace 7 with trace 15 occurs below the level of the

---

Fig. 2–10 *(facing)*. Vasculature of shoot of *Zea mays* (corn, maize). (*A*) Stem with 10 nodes. Median leaf traces (*m*) and larger lateral traces (*l*) occur deep in the stem in part of course. Smaller lateral traces occur entirely in peripheral posi-tion (*p*). Some traces are vestigial (*v*) and are not connected with other bundles. Coleoptile traces at *co*. (*B* and *C*) Same part of the stem showing vascular con-nection between the main and the axillary shoots. Two systems of traces, the outer (*B*) and the inner (*C*), are shown separately. (After Kumazawa [1961].)

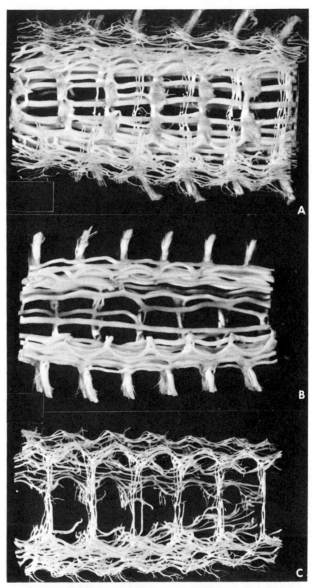

Fig. 2–11. Vascular system from pieces of retted maize ear. (*A*) Entire vascular system. (*B*) The stronger, inner vascular system with the upper surface cut away. (*C*) The weaker outer vascular system with the lower surface split. Slightly magnified. (From Laubengayer, [1949].)

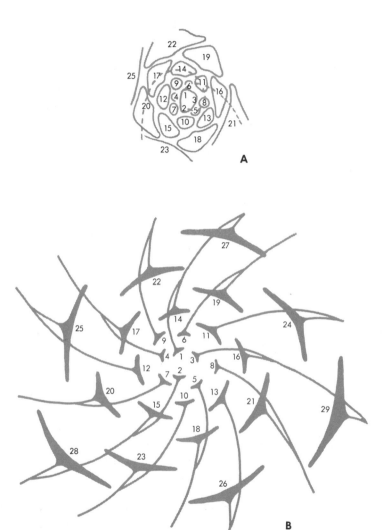

Fig. 2–12. Phyllotaxis and trace relations in *Sequoia sempervirens* shoot. *(A)* Cross section through shoot tip with young leaves numbered from the apex downward. Two contact parastichies are indicated, one with plastochronic intervals of 3, the other of 5. *(B)* Sympodia of leaf traces as though seen from above the shoot tip. The triangular areas indicate leaf bases. The numbering of leaves is the same as in *A*. The plastochronic interval between leaf traces in the sympodia is 13. The sympodia are not interconnected. (Modified after Esau, [1954].)

primary connection of trace 2 with trace 7. Thus the sympodium 15-7 includes also part of trace 2. Farther down the stem the trace complex 15-2-7 is connected with the adjacent 10-2 sympodium (Fig. 2-1, C) in which one half of trace 10 is represented. Through its association with trace 10, the sympodium 15-2-7 is connected with trace 5 also, because this trace is part of the sympodium 5-10-2.

The vascular system of *Hectorella*, as presented in Figure 2-1, illustrates the meaning of a reticulate pattern analyzed in terms of leaf traces. As indicated before, some authors treat the sympodia as independent stem bundles which continue indefinitely in the stem, and from which the leaf traces diverge like branches (Dormer, 1954). It is possible to discuss the vascular organization usefully by employing either the concept of stem bundles or that of leaf-trace sympodia. But developmentally the relation between the leaf traces and the sympodia is more direct than is implied in the concept of independent stem bundles (see Chapters Three and Four).

A comparison of A and C in Figure 2-1 shows that contact parastichies with a plastochronic interval of 5 are those along which the traces have their primary connections. The parastichies of the secondary connections are not contact parastichies; they are rather steep (1-9-17-25). Figures 2-2 and 2-3 give other examples of agreement between one set of contact parastichies and the vascular-connection parastichies in shoots with closed vascular systems (*Linum usitatissimum*). In all three shoots depicted in these figures, the sets of steeper and more numerous contact parastichies (5, Fig. 2-2, A; 8, Fig. 2-2, D; 7, Fig. 2-3, A) are those along which the leaf traces are primarily interconnected. As mentioned earlier, the numbers of contact parastichies in a set also express the plastochronic intervals between two contiguous leaves in the parastichies. Thus, the plastochronic intervals for the primary connections in these shoots are 5, 8, and 7 respectively. The secondary connections occur at plastochronic intervals of 8 (Fig. 2-2, A–C), 13 (Fig. 2-2, D–F), and 11 (Fig. 2-3). These plastochronic intervals are not represented in the contact parastichies of the three shoots. Nevertheless, all series of figures—the numbers of contact parastichies, the intervals between contiguous leaves in these parastichies, and the intervals between leaves primarily and secondarily interconnected by leaf traces—fall into the Fibonacci summation series, either the primary (3-5-8-13. . .; Fig. 2-2) or the secondary (4-7-11-18. . .; Fig. 2-3).

In the transections of stems in Figures 2-2, C and F, and 2-3, C, the leaf traces connected primarily are seen grouped in stem sectors delimited by broken lines. These sectors may be called parastichy sectors. In *Linum*, here depicted, their number agrees with that of parastichies in one of the two sets of contact parastichies. Each parastichy sector contains 3 or 4, rarely 5, bundles in all three types of shoots. Most of these bundles are those that have primary connections within sympodia (primary bundles of the sector), but bundles pertaining to secondary connections (secondary bundles of the sector) are intermingled with the others. In Figure 2-2, C, for example, one parastichy sector contains a set of primary bundles 14-19-24 and a secondary bundle 11. The latter is represented also in the adjacent sector 11-16-21 where 11 constitutes a primary bundle. The two bundles numbered 11 are two halves of a trace sympodium in which 11 was the oldest trace. This sympodium was forked over the gap of leaf 24.

Since the number of bundles per parastichy sector is approximately the same in the three *Linum* shoots, the number of sectors determines the total number of bundles seen in a transection of the stem. Furthermore, since the bundles and the interfascicular regions in the different stems are on the average similar in size, the larger number of bundles must be associated with wider stems. In the *Linum* stems here depicted, the width of stems increases from Figure 2-2, C, to Figure 2-3, C, and is greatest in Figure 2-2, F. The corresponding numbers of parastichy sectors are 5, 7, and 8 and the numbers of bundles to a transection of stem are 18, 26, and 29. Thus, in the same species higher phyllotactic values are associated with wider stems, wider vascular cylinders (that is, wider pith), and a larger number of bundles in a cross section of a stem (Barthelmess, 1935; Camefort, 1956).

Another significant regularity in the comparative structure of the three stems of *Linum* is that the higher phyllotactic values are associated with longer traces as measured by the number of internodes traversed by these traces. This number, of course, corresponds to the plastochronic interval between trace connections. The distance between a leaf insertion and the level at which its trace sympodium branches over a gap of another leaf is also greater in a shoot with higher phyllotactic values. This relation is expressed in the plastochronic interval between a leaf trace confronting a gap and the oldest trace in the sympodium that branches over this gap (13 in Fig. 2-2, C; 21 in Fig. 2-2, F; 18 in Fig. 2-3, C).

During primary growth, the shoot of a plant typically increases in thickness from the base upward (Bower, 1921; Troll and Rauh, 1950). Thus the stem assumes the form of an inverted cone. In plants with secondary growth, the difference in stem thickness between the lower and the upper part is soon effaced because the secondary thickening proceeds from below upward.

Various changes are correlated with primary acropetal increase in thickness of the axis. The principal ones are increase in size of the apical meristem, increase in diameter of pith and of the vascular cylinder, and increase in the number of bundles in the cross section of the stem. These, of course, are changes commonly associated with phyllotactic changes with regard to leaf arrangement and the plastochronic intervals between leaf-trace connections.

In some plants, no phyllotactic changes were observed during the upward primary widening of the axis. In such plants the increase in number of bundles may be related to an increase in the width of leaves and in the number of traces per leaf, as is common in grasses (e.g., Mullendore, 1948). The extension of leaf traces through a larger number of internodes also could result in an increase of the number of bundles, as seen in a transection of a stem, without a change in phyllotaxis. A tangential spread of leaf traces at higher levels of the shoot, perhaps accompanied by a branching of these traces without relation to gaps, would make possible an increase in diameter of the vascular cylinder without a change in phyllotaxis (O'Neill, 1961).

The preceding parts of this chapter illustrate the usefulness of the concept of leaf trace for discussions of phyllotaxis and the various correlated phenomena. But, as indicated previously, the concept of the leaf trace must be used judiciously. If one adheres to the interpretation of the shoot as an organized whole, he will regard the leaf trace as an intrinsic part of this whole. Topographically, the leaf trace is part of the primary vascular system of the stem. If the axis were devoid of leaflike appendages, as is the root axis, for example, no leaf traces as such would differentiate, but vascular tissue would not be absent.

Conceivably, in some seed plants and ferns part of the primary vascular system of the shoot cannot be accounted for in terms of leaf traces (Balfour, 1958; Inouye, 1956; Orsós, 1941-1942). In this respect the dicotyledons with the so-called anomalous structure, especially those having cortical and medullary bundles, in addition to the primary vascular cylinder in the usual position, need a thorough investigation. Our information on the leaf-trace relationship is also rather incomplete with regard to the monocotyledons, particularly the perennial types. An example of a vascular system of a monocotyledon that is difficult to analyze is that of the bulb so characteristic of the Liliales (Mann, 1952). The leaf traces diverge from a complex network in the stem (Fig. 2-13) to which, at lower levels, the traces of the adventitious roots are connected also (Fig. 2-14).

A study of a species of Compositae with medullary bundles (*Dahlia*; Davis, 1961) has shown that the elaborate medullary vascular system present in this plant is connected with the vascular supply of both leaves and axillary buds (Fig. 2-15). The author suggests that the medullary bundles in Compositae originated from a leaf-trace system. This suggestion seems to imply that leaf traces and the primary vascular system in the stem are fundamentally distinct entities, an interpretation not advocated in this book. Rather, it may be said that Davis's work on *Dahlia* pertains to the question of the degree to which the primary vascular system of the stem reflects its association with the leaves. Ontogenetically, and presumably also phylogenetically, the leaf traces are part of the vascular system of the stem. The clarity of the leaf-trace organization in the stem varies in degree and possibly may be obscured, as in *Dahlia*, by secondary evolutionary specializations.

CONCLUSION

In its various manifestations, the phenomenon of phyllotaxis reveals the existence of a distinctive tendency in plants to produce their parts in harmonious regular sequences. The arrangement of leaves and their traces in such a way that numerous sets of parastichies can be recognized in a given shoot is particularly indicative of the intrinsic symmetry in plant structure. The occurrence of symmetry gives one the opportunity to use numerical values for characterizing the arrangement and relationship of parts. Thus, authors may use for such characterizations the contact parastichies

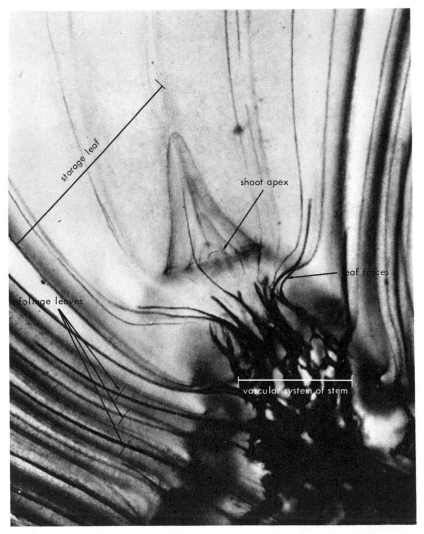

Fig. 2–13. Cleared longitudinal section through base of developing clove of garlic (*Allium sativum*). Traces to leaves diverge from vascular network in stem. (From Mann [1952].)

or the plastochronic intervals within them (Church, 1904; Van Iterson, 1907); or they may select only certain contact parastichies, for example those relating the leaf arrangement to the cotyledons

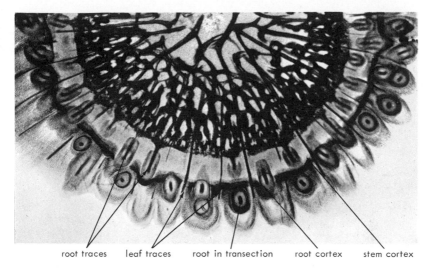

root traces   leaf traces   root in transection   root cortex   stem cortex

Fig. 2–14. Cleared nearly transverse section of mature garlic clove (*Allium sativum*). The vascular system is a network composed of leaf traces and traces of adventitious roots. (From Mann [1952].)

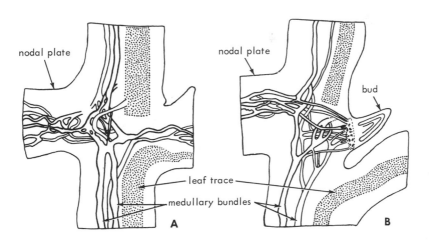

Fig. 2–15. Longitudinal sections of nodes of *Dahlia lehmanni* showing connection of medullary bundles with vasculature of nodal plate and traces of leaf (*A*) and axillary bud (*B*). (After Davis [1961].)

(e.g., Loiseau, 1959; Plantefol, 1947, 1950; see also Cutter, 1959); or they may identify the phyllotaxis on the basis of parastichies along which foliar traces are interconnected (e.g., Esau, 1943a; Tucker, 1961). Debates as to which of these parastichies best expresses the symmetry of a given shoot would seem to be unproductive. Different phenomena may require reference to different sets of parastichies for effective discussions; but, as Erickson (1959) has stressed, it is essential that an author specify the basis he chooses for designating the phyllotaxis of the plant he describes.

chapter three

Initiation of the
Vascular System in
the Shoot

IDENTIFICATION OF PROCAMBIUM

The primary vascular system is initiated in the form of its meristem, the procambium (or provascular tissue). When this meristem is established, it may be recognized in longitudinal sections as strands of elongated cells (Figs. 2-5, C; 2-6; and 2-7). In early stages of procambial differentiation, the elongated form is attained by longitudinal divisions that are followed by little lateral enlargement. Thus, procambial cells become narrower than the adjacent ground-meristem cells (Fig. 2-4). Later, the ground-tissue cells continue to divide transversely (and longitudinally), whereas procambial cells grow in length and thus become longer than the adjacent cells (Fig. 2-7). Procambial cells first appear denser than the more vacuolated cells of the ground tissue, but later they become considerably vacuolated (Fig. 2-7, below).

The procambium differentiates from derivatives of the apical meristem and becomes distinguishable from the ground meristem rather gradually (Figs. 2-5, A and B; and 3-1). Consequently the level of the first stage of procambial differentiation cannot be determined exactly. Determination requires a comprehensive study based on knowledge of phyllotaxis, leaf-trace relationships, plastochronic steps in the development of leaf primordia, and the sequence of histologic changes at the successive levels below the apical meristem. In other words, the initiation of procambium must be studied as one of the elements of differentiation of the shoot as a whole.

Because the apical part of the shoot has practically no internodes and the lateral dimensions also are small, successive sections

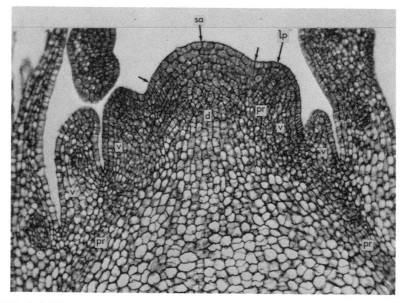

Fig. 3–1. Shoot apex (*sa*) of *Lupinus* with youngest leaf primordium at *lp*. Procambium (*pr*), well defined below, less distinct from adjacent cells higher up. Arrows mark crowding of cells above leaf axils. At *d*, cell division zone above vacuolating pith. At *v*, stages in vacuolation of abaxial parenchyma in leaf primordia. × 74. (Courtesy of T. B. O'Neill.)

may differ from one another considerably in cellular patterns. Thus the study would be unreliable unless serial sections were studied, both transverse and longitudinal.

PROCAMBIUM IN RELATION TO APICAL MERISTEM

In considering the gross aspects of procambial differentiation in the shoot, one can say that the vascular system is initially blocked out among the derivatives of the apical meristem by differential parenchymatization—enlargement and conspicuous vacuolation of cells—of the future ground tissue. At the same level, the prospective vascular region does not undergo parenchymatization but appears cytologically as dense as the densest part of the apical meristem (usually the peripheral part). In other words, it remains eumeristematic, that is, composed of small densely cytoplasmic cells.

The parenchymatization of the ground tissue follows a distinct pattern. In seed plants the pith becomes vacuolated independently of the position of leaf primordia and may begin to assume a parenchymatic aspect below the level of attachment of the youngest primordium (Fig. 3-1), or at that particular level, or above that level. In some ferns (Polypodiaceae) vacuolation of the pith appears to occur in steps in relation to the development of leaf gaps (Kaplan, 1937). In plants with a solid vascular cylinder and no leaf gaps (for example, *Elodea, Hippuris,* and other aquatics; such vascular cryptogams as *Psilotum nudum, Lycopodium, Selaginella,* and some ferns) no pith is formed.

The parenchymatization of the cortex also follows varied patterns. In small-leaved gymnosperms and dicotyledons and in *Equisetum* the cortex becomes vacuolated later than the pith and is at first confluent with the future vascular region; thus the two together appear as a peripheral eumeristematic region (Fig. 3-2, B and C). When the cortex eventually vacuolates in such stems, the differentiating vascular region assumes the form of a ring in transverse sections (Fig. 3-2, E).

In megaphyllous plants vacuolation of the cortical parenchyma is usually correlated with parenchymatization of leaf primordia. Parenchymatic differentiation begins in the leaf primordia (Fig. 3-2, B, leaf 5) before it occurs in the cortex. At lower levels the abaxial parenchyma of the leaf bases (Fig. 3-1, at *v*) is identifiable as cortical parenchyma; the internodes are still too short to permit a distinction between the leaf bases and the stem cortex (Fig. 3-2, C–F). While the vascular region is being delimited by parenchymatization of the cortex, the stem is increasing in width and in length and the differentiating vascular system participates in this growth; this system becomes wider (compare D, E and F in Fig. 3-2) and longer.

The characterization of the initially definable vascular region in terms of procambium constitutes one of the major problems reported in the literature on primary vascular differentiation. As stressed previously, the characteristic narrow elongated form of procambial cells develops gradually. Divisions causally related to the development of this shape are not the only longitudinal divisions occurring in the shoot at that level. Increase in axis circumference involves periclinal longitudinal divisions which may occur alongside those concerned with the formation of procambium (Esau, 1942). In many plants growth of the shoot apex is associated

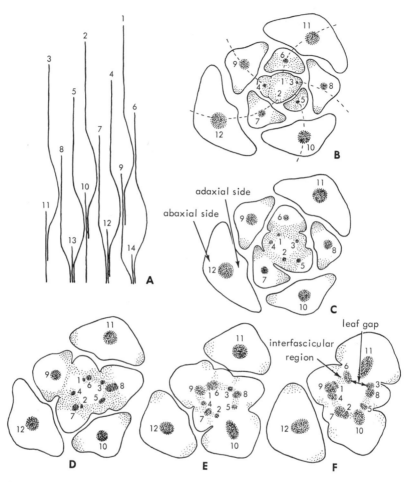

Fig. 3–2. Vasculature of *Taxus baccata* shoot. (*A*) Leaf-trace arrangement. When followed downward, trace *n* connects with trace *n* + 5, then separates from *n* + 5 and fuses with *n* + 8. In the diagram, connections are shown only as approximations. (*B–F*) Successive levels of shoot in cross sections. Leaf traces are numbered beginning with the youngest. One set of contact parastichies is indicated in *B*. (*B–F* after De Sloover [1958].)

with an accumulation of narrow cells resulting from anticlinal divisions in and above the axils of the youngest leaf primordia (Fig. 3-1, unlabeled arrows). These cells are sometimes mistaken for procambial cells. In some species this growth pattern is less conspicuous

(Fig. 2-5, C, arrows), but the cells may retain their elongated shape for some time (Fig. 2-5, A, arrows) and thus complicate the recognition of procambium.

PROCAMBIAL DIFFERENTIATION AND LEAF TRACES

To identify the youngest procambium in the shoot of a seed plant or a fern it is necessary to analyze the eumeristematic region containing the future vascular system with reference to the development of the leaf primordia. The shoot of *Taxus* illustrated in Figure 3-2 may be used to exemplify such an analysis. More or less close to the shoot apex the eumeristematic region ceases to be homogeneous: groups of small cells appear in cross sections beneath the youngest leaf primordia. In Figure 3-2, B and C, these cells are indicated by dense stippling in positions 1 to 5. These groups of cells are cross sections of leaf traces, still in procambial state, to leaves 1 to 5. They are continuous with the procambial bundles of those leaf primordia that are already elevated above the apex (primordia 3 to 5 in Fig. 3-2). But if the leaf is not yet initiated (locus 1 in Fig. 3-2) or barely so (leaf 2 in Fig. 3-2) the procambium is identifiable only in the stem part of the shoot (Fig. 3-2, C). Thus, in this example, the procambium appears in the stem before it does in the leaf; it differentiates acropetally from the stem toward the leaf.

Figure 3-3 illustrates the appearance of the youngest procambium in cross sections of a *Lupinus* shoot. In A of this figure, a group of cells indicated by the arrow was identified as procambium in the base of the leaf primordium shown. This group of cells was continuous through successive cross sections with the more distinct group—leaf trace—of procambial cells in B. Still farther down in the axis (Fig. 3-3, C) the young leaf trace appears in a bias cut between two older traces (*tr*). It was possible to follow the young trace to its connection with one of the older traces and to determine its phyllotactic relation to it. The position of the strand in relation to others and to the leaf primordium in Figure 3-3, A, and the evidence that it was formed by longitudinal divisions (especially clear in Figure 3-3, B) served for the identification of this procambium.

Figure 3-2, *Taxus*, illustrates more completely the relation be-

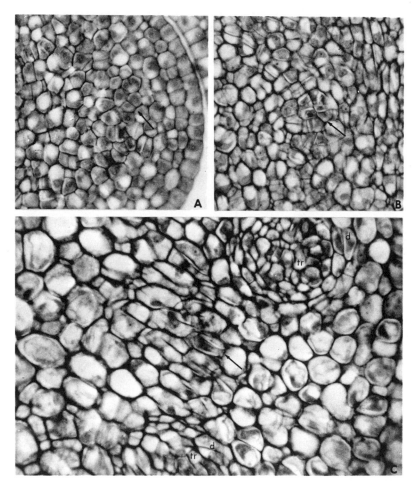

Fig. 3-3. Youngest leaf-trace procambium (marked with an arrow) in *Lupinus* shoot shown at different levels: (*A*) in leaf buttress; (*B*) below leaf buttress; (*C*) lower in the stem, between two older leaf traces (*tr*). Recent divisions have resulted in additions of cells to procambium at *d*. × 500. (Courtesy of T. B. O'Neill.)

tween the differentiation of procambium and the position of the leaf (De Sloover, 1958). When followed in an upward direction, a trace branches from a sympodium in which the next older trace is eight plastochrons older (for example, trace 2 from trace sympodium containing trace 10 in Fig. 3-2, A). Higher up, the trace approaches and almost merges with a sympodium in which the next older trace is five plastochrons older (for example, trace 2 next to sympodium containing trace 7 in Fig. 3-2, A). In transections this relation is depicted for trace 1. In Figure 3-2, E, traces 1 and 6 are in contact, but farther down trace 1 is merged with trace 9. The plastochronic interval of 5 occurs in one of the contact parastichies (Fig. 3-2, B). The other contact parastichy passes through leaves arranged at three plastochronic intervals. The traces are completely fused along a steep parastichy with eight plastochronic intervals in which the leaves are not in contact with one another. The establishment of these phyllotactic relations made it possible to identify the loci of the youngest and the incipient leaf primordia and of their trace procambium in the stem.

The analysis of the *Taxus* shoot in successive cross sections given earlier (Fig. 3-2, B–F) indicates that when the future vascular region becomes delimited beneath the apical meristem by parenchymatization of ground tissue it does not consist of a homogeneous eumeristem but already contains procambial strands. In other words, the earliest procambial strands appear above the level where the vascular region is first blocked out by parenchymatic differentiation of pith and cortex (De Sloover, 1958). These procambial strands are in proper phyllotactic positions to be called leaf traces.

The eumeristematic tissue indicated by the less dense stippling in Figure 3-2, B–F, is not limited to the incipient vascular region. Younger leaves and parts of older leaves and the younger cortex are similarly meristematic. All these regions are continuous with the apical meristem, as may be seen by a comparison of the successive transverse sections. The eumeristematic tissue appears to be a residuum of the apical meristem (Fig. 3-1); it may be called a residual meristem.

As may be seen in Figure 3-2, B–F, the number of procambial strands within the residual meristem of the axis increases in the downward direction. This means that increasing amounts of the residual meristem undergo procambial differentiation. Finally, when all traces and trace sympodia that are characteristic for the shoot in question are formed, the remaining residual meristem differentiates as parenchyma of the gaps (Fig. 3-2, D–F) and the interfascicular regions (these are still meristematic in Figure 3-2, F).

Since the phyllotaxis and the associated phenomena frequently change during the growth of a shoot, the pattern of differentiation established by a comparison of successive levels may not agree in every detail with that characteristic of one level during different stages of development. But the comparison is valid in a general sense. Thus, one can state with reference to vascular differentiation at a given level of shoot that the eumeristematic vascular region usually contains procambial strands by the time it is delimited from the pith and cortex; that the region increases in circumference as does the pith; and that a succession of procambial strands—traces and trace sympodia pertaining to additionally emerging leaves—differentiate in this residual meristem; and that finally portions of the meristem differentiate into parenchyma of gaps and interfascicular regions. If secondary growth is characteristic of the plant, part of the vascular cambium arises within the interfascicular regions and gaps.

SOME INTERPRETATIONS OF PROCAMBIAL INITIATION IN SHOOTS

Although procambial differentiation is often considered in connection with problems of shoot growth, its study is seldom carried out with sufficient completeness to render the interpretations entirely acceptable (see Esau, 1943c, 1954; Gustin and De Sloover, 1955). The initial delimitation of the vascular system in dicotyledons and gymnosperms was considered rather comprehensively by Louis (1935). His main contribution was elucidation of the relation between the leaf primordia and the stem with regard to the vacuolation phenomena that block out the prospective vascular region beneath the apical meristem. Louis termed this region in its earliest stage of development the prodesmogen, rather than the residual meristem. In Louis' view (1935), the prodesmogen constitutes a precursor of desmogen (*desmos*, meaning strand), that is, of procambium. Somewhat earlier than Louis, Helm (1931) treated the same subject by describing a meristem ring as the earliest evidence of vascularization. He characterized this ring not as a special meristem but as a remainder of the apical meristem. Helm did not deal with the relation of leaf primordia to vacuolation of the cortex, but he recognized that the procambium arose as separate bundles in the meristem ring. He thus corrected an older concept which stated that the procambium was at once formed as a continuous ring (see Esau, 1943c).

Kaplan (1936, 1937) used the ideas of Louis and Helm to discuss his developmental concept of the stele and was the author of the term "residual meristem." Although Kaplan considered this meristem to be a residuum of the apical meristem, he recognized the need for qualifying this interpretation because in many apices the distal cells are more highly vacuolated than the residual meristem. The residual meristem is a continuation of the eumeristematic part of the apical meristem, which in many shoots constitutes the peripheral part where the leaf primordia arise.

According to Kaplan, the residual meristem of the shoot axis can appear as a ring, as a peripheral meristem (Fig. 3-2, B), or as a meristematic core (*Elodea, Lycopodium, Selaginella*). In anomalous dicotyledons and certain monocotyledons several concentric rings of the meristem may be present.

Helm, Louis, and Kaplan did not regard the precursor of the vascular region as a distinct meristem. All three authors treat the tissue as one closely related to the apical meristem, a residual meristem in the sense of Kaplan. Some workers, however, stress that the meristem has special characteristics. Hegedüs (1954), for example, holds that the ratio of the diameter of the cell to the diameter of the nucleus definitely distinguishes the precursor of the vascular region from the preceding and the associated meristems.

Kaplan (1937) studied vascular initiation in various groups of plants, including ferns and other vascular cryptogams. In some ferns the vacuolation of pith and cortex resembles that in the seed plants, in others the formation of pith is determined by the vacuolation of leaf-gap parenchyma. But in all types, the precursor of the vascular region is the ontogenetically still undetermined residual meristem according to Kaplan. In contrast, Wardlaw (1952, p. 372) interprets the so-called incipient vascular tissue, or the prestelar tissue, in fern apices definitely as a vascular meristem. Moreover, he depicts this meristem as "a cone of vascular tissue" underlying the apical initial and its immediate derivatives (Wardlaw, 1945). This interpretation appears to be based in part on phylogenetic aspects: steles possessing pith (siphonosteles) are assumed to have evolved from steles without a pith (protosteles). The development of pith and leaf gaps in the solid prestelar tissue is said to be a "real transformation of cells which otherwise would become normal elements of the stele" (Wardlaw, 1945, p. 222). From the ontogenetic aspect this notion of transformation is no more than an assumption; it is not based on ascertained facts. Meristematic cells possess many potentialities, and either pith or cortical parenchyma can form vascular tissues (see Chapter Five). Possession of potentiality to become vascular does not signify that the usual parenchymatic differentiation of pith and cortex involves a transformation from a vascular status. Positional relations play a major role in determining cell differentiation. The evolution of the siphonostelic from the protostelic condition could have resulted in new positional relations which were reflected in different ontogenetic patterns.

In contrast to the view that the procambium originates in an undeterminate residual meristem in relation to leaves (in seed plants and ferns), Bartels (1960) and Kalbe (1962) derive the procambium directly from the apical meristem, from cells in the third or fourth layer from the surface. The interpretations of these authors are based on cell patterns seen in longitudinal views, and they appear as artificial as does Guttenberg's concept (1960, pp. 181, 183) of a procambial histogen having separate initials in the apical meristem. This concept does not agree with the evidence that the vascular and nonvascular tissues are not sharply separated at their origin.

GROWTH OF PROCAMBIUM

Latitudinal growth

When procambial strands are initiated in the residual meristem, an increasing number of cells become involved in longitudinal divisions. Thus, the early transverse growth of the procambium occurs at the expense of the cells surrounding those that began dividing first. At the end of this stage of growth, one daughter cell of the two resulting from a cell division may become incorporated in the procambium, and the other may mature as a ground-tissue cell. Thus, vascular and nonvascular cells are ontogenetically closely related.

One of the elements of the latitudinal growth of the procambial strands is their expansion in tangential extent. In some plants (e.g., tomato, Thompson and Heimsch, 1964; tobacco, Esau,

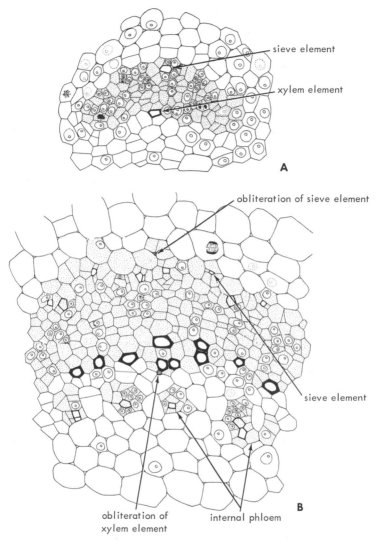

Fig. 3–4. Transections of *Nicotiana tabacum* petioles showing two stages of differentiation of vascular tissues (stippled areas). (*A*) Entire procambial strand with first sieve element and first xylem element mature. (*B*) Part of vascular bundle. From above downward in *B*: external phloem with numerous sieve tubes, one almost obliterated; procambium with radially seriated cells; xylem with numerous tracheary elements (thick walls), the first almost obliterated; internal phloem with some sieve tubes. × 340. (From Esau [1938].)

1938; *Pelargonium*, Blyth, 1958) the procambium assumes a practically continuous appearance as the leaf traces become contiguous during their lateral growth. The common pattern in dicotyledons and conifers, however, is the arrangement of procambium in discrete strands separated by interfascicular regions.

Latitudinal growth through addition of cells on the periphery overlaps with the increase in the number of cells within the procambium and with the beginning of differentiation of vascular elements (Fig. 3-4, A). The predominant planes of divisions within the procambium vary in different plants. They may be variously oriented or they may be mainly periclinal planes. Sometimes the procambium of the future phloem shows no preferred orientation of walls (Fig. 3-4, A) whereas the xylary procambium resembles the vascular cambium in having radially seriated cells (Fig. 3-4, B), a pattern that results from repeated periclinal divisions. Some authors consider that radial seriation of cells in a vascular meristem is an invariable indication of cambial activity and secondary growth. To be useful, the classification into primary and secondary growth should have a broader basis than the single characteristic of cell orientation (see Esau, 1943c). Figures 3-5 and 3-6 compare procambium and cambium of tobacco (*Nicotiana tabacum*). In cross sections (Fig. 3-5) the procambium and the xylem show radial seriation of cells; the phloem has a less orderly arrangement of cells. In the cambium the narrow radial diameters of cells indicate

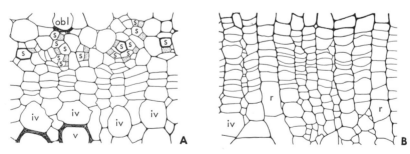

Fig. 3–5. Comparison of procambium (*A*) and cambium (*B*) as seen in transverse sections of stem. *Nicotiana tabacum*. Both meristems show radial seriation of cells. Details: *iv*, immature vessel; *obl*, obliterated phloem elements; *r*, ray; *s*, sieve element; *v*, vessel. Both × 240.

a greater frequency of periclinal divisions than is characteristic of the procambium. In tangential sections, the cambium (Fig. 3-6, B) is organized in two systems, one composed of ray initials, the other of fusiform initials. The procambium has a more homogeneous structure (Fig. 3-6, A). There is a corresponding division into ray and axial (or longitudinal) systems in the secondary xylem and secondary phloem derived from the cambium, and an absence of such division in the primary vascular tissues derived from the procambium.

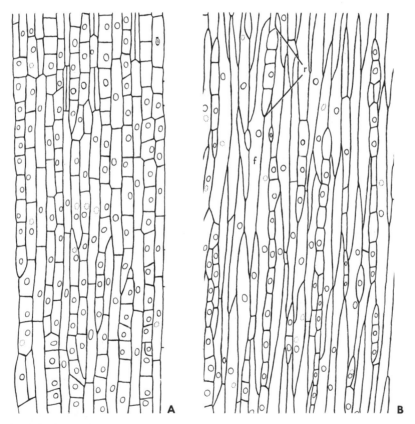

Fig. 3–6. Comparison of procambium (A) and cambium (B) as seen in tangential sections of stem. *Nicotiana tabacum.* Details: f, fusiform initial; r, ray initials. Both × 140.

Longitudinal growth

In the discussion of procambial differentiation in *Taxus* (Fig. 3-2) it was pointed out that although the procambium was absent in the youngest leaf primordia, it was present deeper in the axis, in the leaf-trace positions for these primordia, and that this sequence indicated an acropetal direction of differentiation of the leaf-trace procambium. Since these young leaf traces could be followed downward to their connections with older leaf traces, the differentiation may be characterized as continuous acropetal. Thus, one can visualize the differentiation of new procambial leaf traces as a process of diverging or branching of younger traces from older trace sympodia (Fig. 3-2, A) and their differentiation toward the emerging leaf primordia.

Continuous acropetal differentiation of procambium has been reported for a number of species of dicotyledons and gymnospersms (see reviews by Esau, 1943c, 1954, and Gustin and De Sloover, 1955). The study of this aspect of procambial growth is difficult. In the apical region of the shoot where the primordia arise, the internodes are short or absent, and in the nodal regions the traces have a somewhat oblique course. The procambium could be missed (Fig. 3-3, C, arrow) if serial cross sections were not used and the phyllotactic leaf-trace relationship were not known. In longitudinal sections the recognition of the procambial course is obscured by the presence of leaf gaps. If the section is median with respect to a leaf, it is also median with respect to the gap opposite this leaf, and consequently the procambium located above this gap appears discontinuous below (Fig. 3-7, A). The continuity of the trace procambium near a gap can be recognized only by reference to serial sections (Fig. 3-7, B).

Students of procambial differentiation have observed repeatedly that procambium is associated with the youngest identifiable primordia (Fig. 2-5, B; Bersillon, 1955; De Sloover, 1958; McGahan, 1955; Millington and Gunckel, 1950; and others). Of particular interest is the development of leaf traces before the divisions that initiate the corresponding leaf have taken place. This sequence has been reported for several gymnosperms (*Ginkgo*, Gunckel and Wetmore, 1946a, Hagemann, 1963; *Taxus*, De Sloover, 1958; *Pseudotsuga* and *Sequoia*, Sterling, 1945, 1947). In all of these plants, traces to more than one prospective leaf primordium were

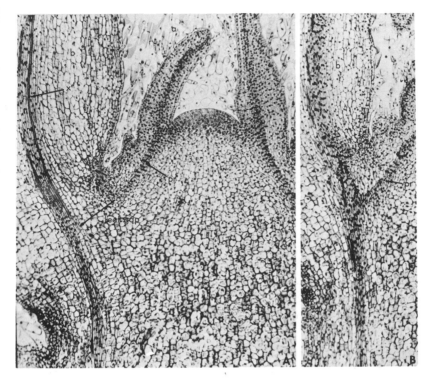

Fig. 3–7. Longitudinal sections of tobacco (*Nicotiana tabacum*) shoot with some of the youngest leaves. The two sections are 20 microns apart. In *A*, leaf *b* is subtended by a gap; in *B*, the section passes laterally from the gap and thus shows the continuity of the procambium (*pr*) to leaf *a* with the procambium to leaf *b*. Xylem element (*x*) is discernible in leaf *b* in *A*. Both × 75.

detected. In *Sequoia* the traces that preceded the primordia in their initial growth had mature phloem in the lower levels of the axis (Sterling, 1946). In *Pseudotsuga* (Sterling, 1947) the number of procambial strands to nonexisting leaves showed seasonal fluctuations: such traces were absent during dormancy, present during growth. Gunckel and Wetmore (1946a) also found the procambium to prospective leaves only in growing buds. A deviating pattern was described for *Abies* (Parke, 1963). In the dormant shoot, five or six existing primordia had no definable trace procambium associated with them. This procambium appeared during the elongation of the shoot.

Precocious differentiation of leaf traces has been reported for some angiosperms, three dicotyledons, *Anagallis, Coleus,* and *Ligustrum* (De Sloover, 1958), and two monocotyledons, *Costus* (Smith, 1941) and *Alstroemeria* (Priestley, Scott, and Gillett, 1935). In *Coleus* and *Ligustrum* the precocious traces had mature phloem at lower levels (De Sloover, 1958).

Monocotyledons typically have more than one trace per leaf and some studies indicate that not all of these traces differentiate acropetally from the stem toward the leaf. According to Kumazawa (1961) and Sharman (1942), for example, in maize (*Zea*) shoots the median leaf trace differentiates acropetally and continuously, but the lateral traces have a bidirectional course, basipetal in the stem, from the leaf base downward, and acropetal in the leaf, from the leaf base upward. According to Masayuki (1962), in the rice (*Oryza*) plant both the median and the lateral traces are initiated at the base of the leaf and differentiate bidirectionally from here. At the same time, procambial strands develop acropetally in the axis and join the basipetally differentiating leaf traces. Rohweder (1963) suspects a basipetal differentiation of procambium in the stem of certain Commelinaceae. (For other examples of monocotyledons see Esau, 1954.) A dicotyledon, *Micropiper excelsum,* with scattered vascular bundles, some of which are not connected with leaves, appears to resemble the monocotyledons in having basipetally differentiating lateral leaf traces (Balfour, 1957, 1958). Some authors maintain that basipetal differentiation of leaf traces is typical, without providing adequate supporting evidence—a level-by-level mapping of leaf traces in relation to the emerging leaf primordia (see Esau, 1954, and Gustin and De Sloover, 1955).

Despite the frequent use of ferns in experimental studies on morphogenesis, vascular differentiation in these plants has not been comprehensively studied. The available literature suggests an acropetal course of differentiation of the procambial system, but the variability and complexity of this system in the ferns does not justify generalization in the absence of extensive comparative studies.

In *Lycopodium* and *Selaginella,* which have no leaf gaps, the central column of procambium differentiates acropetally and reaches levels above the youngest leaf primordia (e.g., Buvat, 1955). Some work has been done on the differentiation of the leaf-trace procambium in these two genera, and in *Equisetum,* but the conclusions are conflicting (see Esau, 1954).

PROCAMBIUM IN LEAF BLADES

The procambium differentiating acropetally in the emerging leaf primordium becomes one of the veins of the leaf. If the leaf has only one trace, this first procambium constitutes the midvein, and the lateral veins may diverge from it in the form of branches. If the leaf has more than one trace, they may continue as independent veins in the blade, or they may anastomose in the petiole. Differentiation of the characteristic venation patterns (netted in most dicotyledons, parallel in most monocotyledons) is correlated with the growth patterns of the leaf blades themselves.

In a dicotyledon leaf as exemplified by *Liriodendron* (Pray, 1955a), secondary veins, which diverge from the midvein, begin to develop soon after marginal growth starts forming the blade. This differentiation occurs in continuity with the midvein. The panels of tissue delimited by the secondary veins—the intercostal panels— become subdivided by tertiary veins (Fig. 3-8, A). As far as was possible to ascertain, these veins appear at once from one secondary vein to another. The quarternary veins delimit polygonal areoles which are subdivided several times by further veins. When the leaf is about 2.5 cm long the vein endings are formed (Fig. 3-8, B). Blind vein endings develop when the smallest bundles fail to differentiate from vein to vein. The concept that blind endings may result from breakage of an originally closed network during the enlargement of mesophyll cells (see Clowes, 1961) is not supported by critical ontogenetic observations (Hara, 1958; Pray, 1963).

The larger veins are formed in leaf tissue of considerable depth that eventually constitutes the vein-rib parenchyma. The smaller veins are imbedded in the mesophyll, and in the species investigated they arise from a single median layer of the blade, one of the layers of the plate meristem, as the mesophyll is termed in its embryonic stage (Fig. 3-9, A). Thus the plate meristem, which is one of the forms of the ground meristem, is the source of both mesophyll and the vascular tissue, another example of the lack of ontogenetic separation between vascular and nonvascular tissues.

In monocotyledons with parallel veins, the primary median

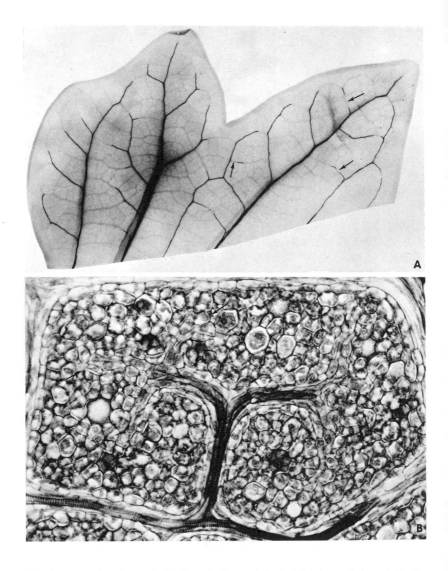

Fig. 3–8. Venation in *Liriodendron* (tulip tree) leaf. (*A*) Piece of cleared blade, stained with safranin which differentiates the secondary walls of the xylem (black). At arrows, discontinuities in the path of xylem differentiation. (*B*) An areole (area delimited by small bundles) with a branched, freely ending vein, still immature at its ends (arrows). *A,* × 17; *B,* × 325. (From Pray [1955a].)

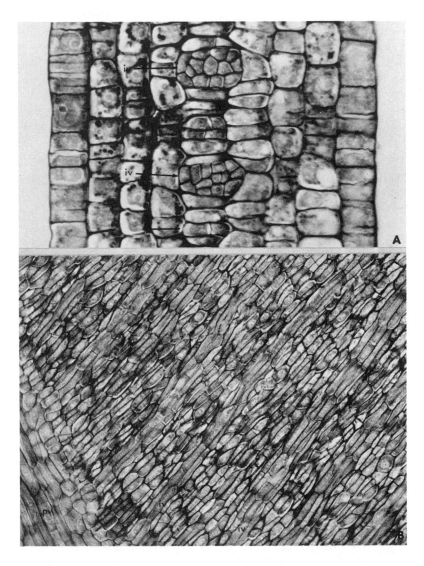

Fig. 3-9. Venation in *Hosta* leaf. Intercostal veins (*iv*) interconnecting primary veins (*pv* in *B*) in transverse (*A*) and longitudinal (*B*) views. The veins are in procambial state. In *A*, two veins are somewhat older (*iv*), two have just started to form (arrows). In *B*, the procambial cells are distinctly longer than adjacent ground parenchyma cells. *A*, × 570; *B*, × 380. (From Pray [1955b].)

55

vein differentiates first, acropetally, and is followed by other primary veins in a marginally directed sequence in relation to the marginal growth of the blade (Pray, 1955b). *Zea* has primary and secondary longitudinal veins, which differ in their course of differentiation (Sharman, 1942). The primary veins differentiate acropetally; the secondary begin at the leaf apex and differentiate basipetally. The longitudinal veins are interconnected by transverse intercostal veinlets. These appear first at the apex of the leaf, then at successively lower levels. In the rice (*Oryza*) leaf there are also two sets of longitudinal bundles, one differentiating acropetally, the other basipetally (Maeda, 1962).

As investigated in *Hosta* (Pray, 1955b) the intercostal veins arise in a single layer of the plate meristem (Fig. 3-9, A). The cells of this meristem are at first polygonal. Then they begin to divide, mainly at right angles to the primary veins, and become elongated. Certain series of these cells gradually assume procambial characteristics by division and elongation (Fig. 3-9, B). This is a subtle and gradual process and appears to occur simultaneously through the entire distance between two primary veins. A comparison of *Hosta* with *Liriodendron* indicates that the divisions in the plate meristem resulting in the appearance of procambium may be more (*Hosta*, Fig. 3-9, B) or less (*Liriodendron*, Fig. 3-8, B) oriented in conformity with the orientation of the future procambium. *Quiina* furnishes another example of highly oriented divisions giving rise to procambium within the plate meristem (Foster, 1952).

Two detailed studies provide a comparison of development of venation in ferns (Pray, 1960, 1962) with that in angiosperms. In *Nephrolepis* and *Regnellidium* marginal growth of the pinna, based on precisely dividing marginal initials, establishes rows of cells whose arrangement foreshadows that of the procambium of the secondary veins. A cytological differentiation of ground-meristem cells—vacuolation and accumulation of tannins—sets off panels of procambial cells. These remain embryonic in appearance until they become longer. The marginal meristem widens and as a result the procambial panels also become wider. Then some derivatives of the marginal meristem differentiate as parenchyma cells within a procambial panel and bring about a dichotomizing of the panel. Marginal growth continues until all the procambial system is laid down. In the angiosperms only the major veins are formed during marginal growth of the blade whereas the smaller veins differentiate during the later intercalary growth of the derivatives of the marginal meristems.

PROCAMBIUM OF BUDS

Axillary buds

As described previously, the traces of axillary buds are leaf traces in the sense that they form the vascular supply of the prophylls on the bud, sometimes also of the leaves placed higher. The timing and direction of differentiation of these traces during formation of the connection between the bud and the main shoot vary in relation to the character of the bud. If a bud is initiated close to the apical meristem and soon begins to develop into a branch, its traces are commonly derived from a residual meristem in the manner described for the leaf traces of the main shoot. The distance between such a bud and the vascular region of the shoot is so short that it is often difficult to recognize whether the differentiation of the procambium occurs from the main axis toward the bud (acropetal differentiation) or from the bud toward the main axis (basipetal differentiation). In many plants this differentiation was interpreted as acropetal (e.g., De Sloover, 1958; Garrison, 1949b; Sacher, 1955b; see also reviews by Esau, 1954, and Philipson, 1949). In other plants the direction was not determined (e.g., Garrison, 1949a; Esau, 1954).

If an axillary bud is initiated rather late or is not immediately connected by traces to the main axis, the tissue beneath the bud becomes vacuolated and parenchymatic, and the procambium eventually differentiates basipetally. Kumazawa (1961), for example, observed that the vegetative axillary buds in maize are initiated far from the shoot apex and are connected to the main axis by basipetal differentiation of procambium. The staminate spikelets, on the other hand, arise close to the apex and appear to be connected to the procambium of the rachis from the beginning. Gifford (1951) reported that the procambial strands of the axillary buds in *Drimys* were differentiating basipetally through vacuolated cells, but that later procambial development also occurred acropetally from the procambium of the main axis. Vaughan (1955) interpreted the differentiation of bud-trace procambium in *Arabidopsis, Capsella,* and *Anagallis* as basipetal. Both Gifford and Vaughan characterized the buds they studied as detached meristems, that is, meristems derived from the apical meristem but separated from it by vacuolated cells. Development of axillary buds from detached meristems, and a basipetal differentiation of their vascular connection with the main axis, were earlier described for the rhizome of the fern *Matteuccia* (Wardlaw, 1943a).

Adventitious buds

Adventitious buds are buds that are not formed in the normal course of shoot growth, as shoot primordia in the axils of developing leaves, but appear some time later on various plant parts other than leaf axils. They appear spontaneously or may be induced to develop by experimental techniques. The development of adventitious buds has been studied in connection with work on growth-regulating substances and other experimental treatments (see Wardlaw, 1952). Adventitious buds typically form their connection with the vascular system of the parent structure by basipetal differentiation of procambium. This kind of pattern was observed in flax buds, which arise in the epidermis of the hypocotyl and are capable of developing into shoots after the seedling is decapitated (Gulline, 1960; Link and Eggers, 1946). Basipetal differentiation of procambium was recorded for adventitious buds on decapitated cranberry seedlings (Bain, 1940), epicotyls of *Linaria* (Champagnat, 1955), leaves of tomato (Fukumoto, 1960), and various organs of other plants (see Esau, 1954). Kondrat'eva-Mel'vil' (1957) found that the character of vascularization of adventitious shoots on roots depends on the position of the bud, its vigor of growth, and anatomy of the root. In buds arising near the cambium, the vascular connection is formed by an acropetal differentiation; in those developing near the periphery of the root, it is formed by basipetal differentiation. Slow-growing buds are vascularized by acropetal differentiation, fast-growing buds by basipetal growth. Buds developing through experimental induction in ferns form a connection with the vascular system of the rhizome by basipetal differentiation (Wardlaw, 1943a,b). If these buds arise in more mature parts of the axis, the basipetally differentiating traces do not reach the vascular system of the main axis, but the buds form their own roots.

PROCAMBIUM OF REPRODUCTIVE SHOOTS

Vascularization of the flower is frequently considered in studies pertaining to its phylogeny and taxonomy. But most of these studies deal with mature flowers. One of the important topics in discussion of floral vascularization is the nature of the flower; specifically, whether the flower is homologous with a vegetative shoot or whether it is a structure that has evolved independently. Proponents of the view that the flower is basically similar to the vegetative shoot regard the vascular region of the flower as a stele with gaps and with traces to the various floral organs. Typically, these organs are crowded on the floral axis (receptacle), and consequently the vascular system is condensed and difficult to analyze in terms of traces and gaps (e.g., Moseley, 1961; Nast, 1944; Sporne, 1958). The similarity between the flower and the vegetative shoot is questioned by some authors on developmental grounds also (see Gifford, 1954). But fundamentally the phenomena of initial vascularization of the inflorescence and the flower can be described in the same terms as those used for the vegetative shoot; and the connection of the reproductive bud with the vascular system of the parent shoot brings up the same questions as that of the vegetative axillary bud.

Phyllotactic patterns can be recognized in the arrangement of floral parts and in the interconnection of their traces (e.g., Tucker, 1961). The phyllotaxis may change when the vegetative stage is succeeded by the reproductive. According to Gifford and Tepper (1961), the rate of production of leaves in *Chenopodium* changes from less than one per day to more than two per day during transition to photoinduced reproductive stage—a phenomenon associated with a change in phyllotaxis.

In studies of several inflorescences, Philipson (1946, 1947a,b, 1948) observed an initial blocking out of the prospective vascular region by vacuolation of the ground meristem. Later, an acropetal differentiation of procambium of the traces to the inflorescence bracts occurred through the residual meristem. With regard to flowers themselves, some authors indicate an acropetal procambial differentiation, others find it to be bidirectional, at least for some floral parts; still others are not certain about the direction. The congested arrangement of floral parts obviously makes the course difficult to ascertain (see Esau, 1954). Procambial differentiation appears to be delayed in relation to some flower parts and occurs within a rather vacuolated tissue (Boke, 1949; Lawalrée, 1948).

CONCLUSION

The review presented in this chapter indicates that many uncertainties exist regarding steps in the initial development of the vascular system in the shoot and the meaning of the observed variations in the pattern of this development. The concept that the vascular tissue might be derived from cells in a specific position in the apical meristem, cells even possibly having the nature of independent initials, finds no support in the more critical studies on vascularization and in the presently available information on the structure and function of the apical meristem (see Clowes, 1961, and Gifford, 1954). Although the epidermis may be derived from a separate cell layer in the apex, the histogenetic relation of the inner tissues to the apical meristem is variable, and ontogenetically the vascular and nonvascular tissues are closely related. This relation is expressed, first, in the gradual delimitation of the future vascular region from the ground tissue by the more rapid differentiation of that tissue. Secondly, it is evident in the origin of procambium in the seed plants (and certain other plants) in relation to the emerging leaf primordia. The close ontogenetic relation between vascular and nonvascular tissue is particularly clear in the development of the venation in the leaf blades. The pattern of vascular initiation is determined by the specific organization of the plant. In the so-called microphyllous plants a column of procambium differentiates independently of the leaves, in the megaphyllous plants the leaves exert a major influence on the form and pattern of differentiation of the vascular system of the shoot. The longitudinal course of procambial growth shows significant variations. The possible meaning of these variations is discussed in connection with the review of the experimental work on vascularization (see pages 95 and 100).

chapter four Primary Xylem and
Phloem in the Shoot

RECOGNITION OF XYLEM AND PHLOEM ELEMENTS

In discussions of primary vascular differentiation in shoots, three phenomena must be considered separately, the differentiation of the procambium (Chapter Three), the maturation of certain procambial cells into xylem elements, and the maturation of other procambial cells into phloem elements. With regard to both xylem and phloem the decision whether a given vascular tissue is present or absent is based on the recognition of conducting elements, tracheary elements (tracheids or vessel members) in the xylem, and sieve elements (sieve cells or sieve-tube members) in the phloem.

In the earliest xylem, in which the tracheary elements are usually accompanied by thin-walled parenchyma cells, these elements are readily distinguishable by their lignified secondary walls (Fig. 3-4) of varied patterns (Figs. 4-1 to 4-4). To determine whether or not the elements are mature, the condition of their protoplasts must be known. Until the secondary wall is fully developed, the tracheary elements maintain living protoplasts with nuclei (Figs. 4-3 and 4-4) and various cytoplasmic structures visible with the electron microscope (Fig. 4-5). After this stage the protoplasts disintegrate.

The conducting elements of the phloem are less readily distinguished because they have no rigid secondary walls of characteristic patterns. But they frequently have thicker and more deeply staining walls than the associated parenchymatic or procambial cells (Fig. 3-4). Their protoplasts remain alive but become enucleate and assume certain peculiar cytophysiologic characteristics. The light staining of these protoplasts is a particularly helpful characteristic (Fig. 4-6). The sieve areas, through which the protoplasts of con-

61

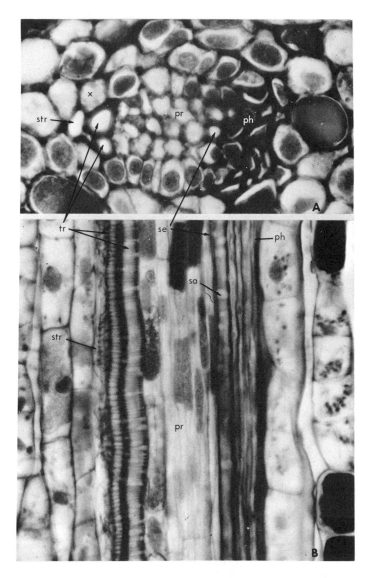

Fig. 4–1. Initial differentiation of vascular bundle in *Abies* shoot in transverse (*A*) and longitudinal (*B*) sections. Details: *ph*, phloem; *pr*, procambium; *sa*, sieve area; *se*, sieve element; *str*, stretched tracheid; *tr*, tracheid; *x*, xylem. *A*, × 610; *B*, × 330. (From Parke [1963].)

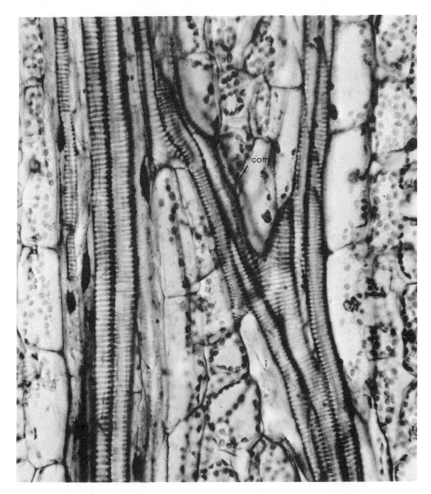

Fig. 4–2. Section of seedling leaf of *Yucca*, parallel to the surface. Illustrates commissural veinlet (*com*) connecting two parallel longitudinal veins. The tracheary elements have helical thickenings. At *i*, immature tracheary element still without secondary walls. No phloem in this view. × 525. (From Arnott [1962].)

tiguous sieve elements are interconnected, are usually small and not distinctly differentiated in the earliest sieve elements (Fig. 4-1). Staining for callose (see Esau, 1961) and use of high magnifications are necessary for their recognition. The association of sieve elements with companion cells in the angiosperms (Fig. 3-5, A) is sometimes used for recognition of these elements, but in the early phloem, companion cells may be absent or, in leaf blades, the companion cells may not be readily distinguishable from other parenchymatic cells associated with the sieve elements (Fig. 4-6).

The recognition of the first vascular elements is particularly critical if the longitudinal course of their differentiation is to be determined. As in procambial studies, the search must be made in unbroken series of serial sections and the units containing these elements must be mapped level by level in relation to leaf pri-

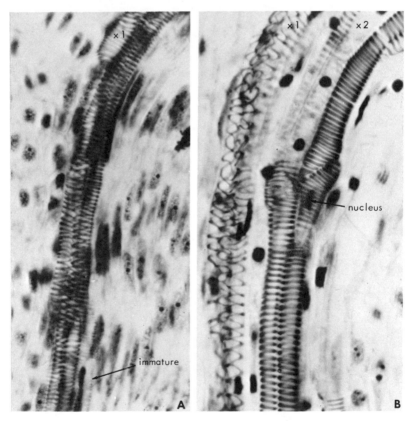

Fig. 4–3. Xylem of leaf traces of *Clematis*, younger (*A*) and older (*B*), in longitudinal views. The xylem in *A* was the first to mature in the trace. Similar xylem in *B*, numbered *x*1, became stretched during internodal elongation. In the meantime xylem *x*2 differentiated. Both × 490.

mordia. For xylem studies, cleared tissues may be successfully used for the recognition of a number of features of the longitudinal course of differentiation (De Sloover, 1958; Jacobs and Morrow, 1957).

Some authors consider that loci of greatest numbers of elements in a mature bundle, as seen in transection, indicate loci of initial differentiation (e.g., Miller and Wetmore, 1946). This criterion is not necessarily reliable. Local increase in numbers of vascular elements may be associated with a specialized structure. The nodal xylem, for example, sometimes has enlargements consisting

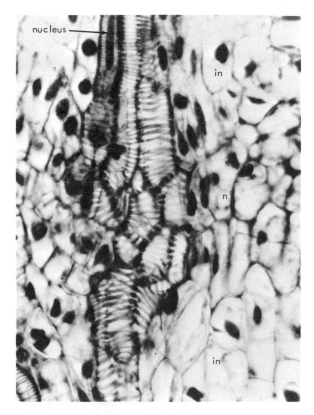

Fig. 4–4. Longitudinal section of leaf trace xylem of *Clematis* showing short xylem elements of the nodal (*n*) region. The elements are much longer in the internode (*in*, shown only in part). × 490.

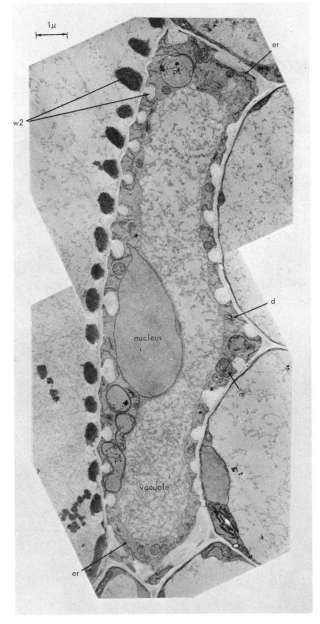

Fig. 4–5.

of short elements (Fig. 4-4), and the number of tracheary elements in a leaf trace may be especially high at the base of the leaf (Rouschal, 1940).

In critical studies on vascularization, the conducting elements are recorded in their different ontogenetic stages, for in a given longitudinal file of cells, mature and immature conducting elements may alternate—a feature that affects the interpretation of differentiation as continuous or discontinuous. Jacobs and Morrow (1957), for example, classified the vessel members as having contents and primary walls only, contents and secondary walls, and no contents in presence of secondary walls. With regard to phloem, presence or absence of nuclei gives a reliable distinction between mature and immature elements but requires the examination at high power of every section of a given sieve element.

In studies on degree of continuity of differentiation, it is often necessary to observe lateral connections between bundles. Figure 4-2 illustrates such a connection (commissure) between two longitudinal bundles in a leaf. In transverse sections an oblique connection (Fig. 4-2) would be cut on bias. Continuous series of sections are necessary for the recognition of connections between bundles, especially in the higher levels of the shoot.

ONTOGENETIC CHARACTERISTICS OF THE FIRST VASCULAR TISSUES

In the common type of shoot in which internodal elongation constitutes part of primary growth, the first phloem and xylem elements mature before this elongation is completed. The nonliving tracheary elements and the enucleate sieve elements are incapable of keeping pace with the elongation by active growth; they are passively stretched. This stretching results in complete destruction

---

Fig. 4–5 (*facing*). Electron micrograph of longitudinal section of tracheary element from small vein in leaf of *Beta* (sugar beet). The element has nonlignified secondary wall ($w2$, white). The adjacent mature tracheary element shown in part to the left has lignified secondary wall ($w2$, black). In both cells the secondary wall forms a spiral pattern (seen in section). Cytoplasmic details: d, dictyosome; er, endoplasmic reticulum; m, mitochondrion; pl, plastid; $w2$, secondary wall. Potassium permanganate fixation.

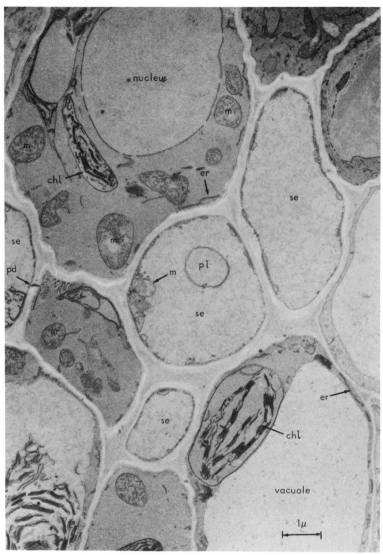

Fig. 4–6. Electron micrograph of cross section of phloem from a small vein in leaf of *Beta* (sugar beet). Sieve elements with clear contents at *se*. Associated nucleate cells have extremely dense cytoplasm. Details: *chl*, chloroplast; *er*, endoplasmic reticulum; *m*, mitochondrion; *pd*, plasmodesma; *pl*, plastid. Potassium permanganate fixation.

of the first conducting elements (Fig. 3-4, B), and the function of conduction is taken over by subsequently differentiating elements.

Figure 4-1 illustrates some of the developmental features just described by reference to a young vascular bundle of *Abies*, a conifer. In both sections, transverse (Fig. 4-1, A) and longitudinal (Fig. 4-1, B), the phloem (*ph*) on the extreme right is no longer in functioning state; it is collapsed. To the left of this phloem the sieve elements (*se*) are still open and their sieve areas (*sa*) are discernible. On the xylem side, stretched (*str*) nonfunctioning elements appear to the left. Later-formed tracheary elements (*tr*) are intact. Additional phloem and xylem elements would have differentiated from the procambium (*pr*) in the middle of the bundle. The figures explain the meaning of centripetal (phloem) and centrifugal (xylem) direction of differentiation. The earlier phloem elements (crushed) are farther from axis center than the later ones (*se*). In the xylem, the earlier elements (*str*) appear closer to the center of the axis than the later elements (*tr*).

Tracheary elements that differentiate in a region subject to elongation have secondary walls of the extensible type, that is, in the form of rings or spirals. The stretching ability of spiral thickenings is illustrated in Figure 4-3. The first tracheary elements in the leaf trace in Figure 4-3, A, are still intact; in Figure 4-3, B, similar elements (*x*1) have much extended spirals, whereas the later-formed xylem (*x*2) is still intact.

The distinction between the earlier and the later primary vascular tissues is usually not sharp. But in ontogenetic studies it is convenient to use separate terms for them, *protoxylem* and *protophloem* for the earlier, *metaxylem* and *metaphloem* for the later vascular tissues. These terms are variously used in the literature (see Bierhorst, 1960, and Esau, 1943c), sometimes with emphasis on one or another characteristic. The terms are most useful if they are applied chiefly to indicate the temporal and positional characteristics of the two parts of the vascular tissues. The protophloem and protoxylem initiate vascular differentiation; they occur in peripheral position with regard to subsequently developing vascular cells. Positional relation is important ontogenetically and phylogenetically for the recognition of exarchy (earliest xylem is farthest from axis center) and endarchy (earliest xylem is nearest the axis center) with regard to the xylem; and it is involved in the development of the concept of leaf trace (as discussed later in this chapter). The positional relation of the protophloem, on the other hand, has a bearing on the delimitation of the vascular region from the cortex and on the concept of pericycle.

In normally elongating shoots, conducting elements of the protophloem and protoxylem are destroyed during the elongation, but the relation between maturation of the first vascular elements and elongation growth is not constant for all parts of the same plant, and it varies in different plants. Similarly, the presence of extensible secondary walls (Fig. 4-3) is not a constant characteristic of the first tracheary elements. For example, they may have non-extensible scalariform or reticulate types of wall in the nonelongating nodal region (Fig. 4-4), as contrasted with cells with spiral thickenings in the internode. Furthermore, extensible types of walls may be present in variable numbers of xylem elements differentiating after the elongation. Thus, the inclusion of wall characteristics or the reference to maturation before elongation in the definition of protoxylem would reduce the usefulness of the term. Protophloem and protoxylem are simply the initial vascular tissues of a system whose character they define by their position. The protoxylem indicates whether the system is endarch or exarch and both tissues indicate whether the system differentiates in relation to leaves or independently of them. Metaxylem and metaphloem succeed the two initial tissues.

Secondary walls in xylem and elongation of shoot

The relation between type of secondary wall in primary xylem and elongation of the organ in which this xylem occurs has been studied by a number of investigators. According to Scherer (1904), strongly elongating roots such as aerial roots or roots growing in moist loose soil have annular and spiral thickenings in the protoxylem; in slowly growing roots this tissue has more continuous types of thickenings. Goodwin (1942) and Stafford (1948) were able to affect the number of xylem elements with extensible walls in grass seedlings by regulating the light. More elements had annular and spiral thickenings in seedlings whose elongation was stimulated by darkness; in the light, reticulate and pitted elements soon succeeded the others. Jacobs (1947) found a correlation between absence of reticulate and pitted walls and the occurrence of rapid elongation in the gynophore of the peanut plant. Investigators discuss speculatively whether the rigid nonextensible types of wall appear when elongation ceases or whether the development of these walls causes the elongation to cease.

Extension and destruction of the first xylem are striking in plants with strongly expressed intercalary growth. Thus, in *Welwitschia*, in which the leaf tissues arise from a basal meristem that functions for many years, the spirally thickened elements traversing the meristem are constantly torn and replaced by new ones (Rodin, 1958). The question may be raised whether the replacement always keeps pace with the destruction. Buchholz (1920) found a variable relation in certain monocotyledons. In some (for example, *Tradescantia*) new xylem was not immediately produced after the destruction of the first xylem in the intercalary growth region, and the lacuna that appeared in the place of the broken-down xylem served—as revealed by a test with dyes—for conduction of water.

Protophloem and pericycle

Destruction of the conducting cells in the first phloem is a well-known phenomenon, but it is not always recognized by investigators because of the small size and short functioning period of the first sieve elements. The common failure to identify the protophloem has led to a major misconception concerning the nature of the region called pericycle. According to the concept of the stele, the pericycle constitutes a ground-tissue portion of the stele. As mentioned in Chapter One, however, in the conifers and in the majority of dicotyledons, the tissue located on the periphery of the vascular cylinder next to the cortex is part of the phloem (Blyth, 1958; Esau, 1950; Léger, 1897; Ozenda, 1949). In many dicotyledons, cells associated with the first sieve tubes differentiate as fibers, the protophloem fibers (for example, Esau, 1943b).

LONGITUDINAL COURSE OF DIFFERENTIATION: AN EXAMPLE

Figure 4-7 is a diagrammatic representation of the main features of the longitudinal course of initial differentiation of xylem and phloem. It is based on composite data collected in studies of vascularization of vegetative shoots of *Coleus blumei* by De Sloover

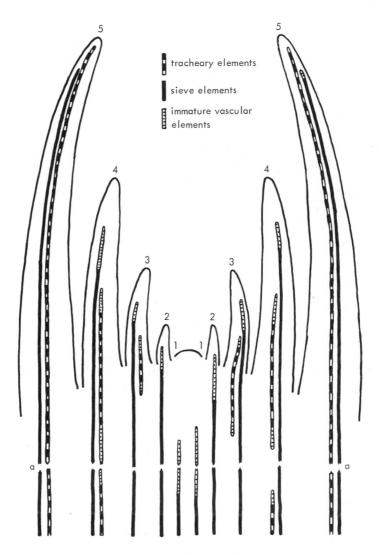

trackeary elements

sieve elements

immature vascular
elements

Fig. 4–7. Diagram exemplifying differentiation of the first phloem and xylem in a dicotyledon shoot with decussate phyllotaxy. The leaves belonging to the same pair bear the same numbers. Although in the shoot the leaf pairs alternate at right angles, they are depicted in the same plane in the drawing. The diagram is based on composite data obtained from a study of vascularization of *Coleus* shoot. At *aa* part of the axis was omitted. (After De Sloover [1958].)

(1958). Although the leaves are decussate, the leaf pairs are drawn in one plane, and the occurrence of two traces to each leaf is ignored. Portions of the bundles are omitted at plane *a-a*.

The general features illustrated are (1) appearance of phloem before xylem in a leaf trace; (2) acropetal differentiation of phloem from the axis toward the leaf; (3) initiation of xylem near the base of the leaf and its subsequent bidirectional differentiation. These features have been observed in many seed plants. Acropetal differentiation of xylem from the axis (traces to leaf pairs 4 and 5), in addition to the bidirectional one from the leaf base, occurs in some plants and not in others.

Figure 4-7 indicates the development of phloem in leaf traces to prospective leaves (pair 1) as reaching the level of 500-600 μ below the apex. In leaf pair 2, immature phloem elements had reached the leaf bases. This event was soon followed by initiation of xylem near the base of the leaf (pair 3). In pair 4 the xylem was still discontinuous in the leaf to the right but had become connected (by immature elements) with the acropetally differentiating xylem in the leaf to the left. The xylem was continuous in leaf pair 5 and had advanced to a higher level of the leaf than had the phloem, another common feature in dicotyledons.

Jacobs and Morrow (1957, 1958) have carried out a precise study of vascularization in *Coleus blumei* by relating the initial differentiation of xylem and phloem to the length of the leaf. The plants used were of one vegetatively propagated clone grown under uniform, controlled conditions, and the collections were made at regular intervals during the day and the night.

A close quantitative relation existed between the length of the leaf and the particular stage of development of xylem and phloem. The leaf (pair 2) was 400-500 μ long when the first sieve element differentiated in it. The sieve elements differentiated quickly, in terms of increasing leaf length, to within 142 μ of the leaf apex, and they maintained this position with remarkable constancy while the leaf increased thousands of microns in length.

Xylem differentiation started in an isolated locus in relation to a leaf (pair 3) 1300 μ long. During the acropetal progress of this xylem, elements with secondary walls reached 700 μ below the leaf tip and maintained this position until the basipetally differentiating xylem established a connection with the mature xylem in the stem.

At this time the leaf was more than twice as long (3000 μ) as when the xylem was initiated, and the acropetal differentiation of the xylem was suddenly accelerated. It reached to within 100 μ from the tip and surpassed the phloem in its acropetal progress.

Jacobs and Morrow (1957) discovered a not previously described locus of xylem initiation in some collections made at night. This locus occurred within the stem at the next node down from the leaf which was soon to have xylem in its base. Thus the initiation in the stem preceded that in the leaf. The two loci of xylem initiation were quickly joined by differentiation of xylem elements in the intervening part of the procambium. (This stage of differentiation is not shown in Figure 4-7.) In the meantime, xylem had been differentiating acropetally in the lower part of the leaf trace of the third leaf, starting from the connection of this trace with an older trace with continuous mature xylem. With the establishment of xylem connection between the upper and the lower part of the trace, leaf 3 acquired continuous xylem. It also became leaf 4, for a new pair of primordia arose at the apex. The two traces of the same leaf had somewhat different patterns of xylem differentiation. The isolated locus in the leaf occurred in one trace; in the other, the xylem differentiated acropetally from the locus one node below; and the traces of both members of a pair of leaves developed xylem at different rates. The authors relate the pattern of xylem differentiation to possible local increases of concentration of auxin, a "piling up at a physiological barrier" as represented by a node (Jacobs and Morrow, 1957, p. 841).

LONGITUDINAL COURSE OF DIFFERENTIATION: COMPARISONS

First xylem and phloem

The general sequence of vascular initiation described for *Coleus*—phloem differentiation following that of procambium in acropetal direction and a later, localized xylem initiation in relation to leaves—was recorded in a number of dicotyledons of different families: *Anagallis* and *Ligustrum* (De Sloover, 1958), *Xanthium* (McGahan, 1955), *Linum* (Esau, 1943a; Girolami, 1953), *Helianthus* and *Sambucus* (Esau, 1945), *Phlox* (Miller and Wetmore, 1946), and others (see Gustin and De Sloover, 1955); and it was described for one monocotyledon (*Zea*, Sharman, 1942). Deviations in details that were encountered do not negate the generalization given above. Among such deviations is the occurrence of a second locus of xylem initiation in the stem as described by Jacobs and Morrow (1957). Others are the acropetally differentiating xylem initially connected with that of an older trace (*Coleus*, *Anagallis*, De Sloover, 1958) and the occurrence of a second locus of xylem initiation near the apex of the leaf (*Ligustrum*, De Sloover, 1958). Then, differentiation within the files of xylem and phloem elements may be discontinuous in the sense that for a time immature elements are interpolated among mature ones (Fig. 4-8; De Sloover, 1958; Esau, 1945).

The pattern of differentiation of the first xylem and phloem elements in gymnosperms resembles that in angiosperms (*Abies*, Parke, 1963; *Pseudotsuga* and *Sequoia*, Sterling, 1946, 1947; *Taxus*, De Sloover, 1958; cataphylls in *Pinus*, Sacher, 1955a; *Ginkgo*, Gunckel and Wetmore, 1946b). Recognition of phloem initiation in this group of plants is rather problematical because the first sieve elements are poorly differentiated. They may belong to the type of tissue called precursory phloem in which nuclei are incompletely degenerated and sieve areas are inconspicuous or not identifiable (Esau, Cheadle, and Gifford, 1953). In xylem differentiation, discontinuities or multiple loci of initiation were recognized (De Sloover, 1958; Sterling, 1946); in *Ginkgo*, acropetally differentiating series of tracheary elements were found advancing toward the series developing basipetally from the leaf (Gunckel and Wetmore, 1946b).

The scanty information on vascular cryptogams (see Esau, 1954) suggests that in the representatives without leaf gaps, such as *Lycopodium* and *Selaginella*, the xylem and the phloem differentiate acropetally in the central column of procambium. In *Equisetum* both tissues are initiated in the nodes in isolated loci and differentiate bidirectionally upward toward the leaves and downward in the subjacent internode (Golub and Wetmore, 1948). With regard to plastochronic timing, the first phloem matures in the third or fourth node from the apex, the first protoxylem in the fourth to seventh nodes. With regard to ferns, some papers report an acropetal differentiation of both kinds of tissue, with the phloem maturing closer to the apical meristem than does the xylem (see

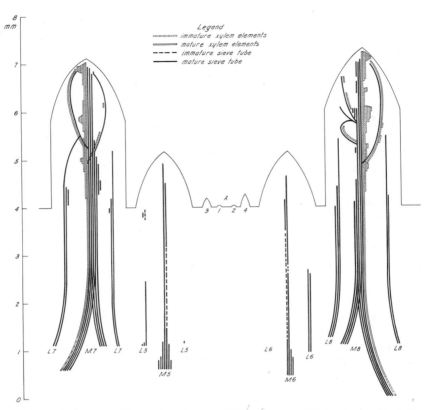

Fig. 4–8. Diagram illustrating the longitudinal course of development of the first phloem and xylem in a *Helianthus* shoot. Leaves are numbered beginning with the youngest and are shown spread in one plane. The xylem in leaves 7 and 8 had no mature connection with xylem in the stem below. (From Esau [1945].)

Esau, 1954). According to Iossa (1914), in *Osmunda* the protoxylem is initiated in the leaf traces.

Later xylem and phloem

Most of the studies on the longitudinal vascular differentiation deal with the protoxylem and protophloem and frequently only with the first few elements of these tissues. In *Linum* (Esau, 1943a), *Coleus* (De Sloover, 1958; Jacobs and Morrow, 1957), *Ligustrum* and *Taxus* (De Sloover, 1958), several longitudinal files of xylem were found to have similar discontinuous initiation and further bidirectional differentiation. De Sloover (1958) interprets the elements succeeding the very first as metaxylem elements, without defending this classification. In following the later differentiation of phloem, De Sloover (1958) found some sieve tubes, with immature elements at both ends, located in the leaf trace near the level of maximal differentiation of xylem. He interpreted these sieve tubes as pertaining to metaphloem and concluded that their isolation indicated a bidirectional differentiation of metaphloem.

As stated earlier, the means of delimiting the meta-tissues from the proto-tissues are not clear. If a delimitation is attempted in a given plant, the primary vascular differentiation of this plant must be known completely from the initiation of the first elements to the beginning of secondary growth, or the termination of primary growth if no secondary tissues are formed; and the vascularization must be related to the primary elongation of the plant. This information is not available for the plants studied by De Sloover, and therefore his investigation leaves the question open regarding the course of differentiation of metaxylem and metaphloem. The bidirectional differentiation of phloem he reported may have been related solely to augmentation of vascular tissues at nodes. A vascular bundle may be twice as wide at the base of a leaf as it is immediately above and below (Rouschal, 1940).

As has been shown in Chapter Three the first procambium visible beneath the shoot apex in a seed plant is leaf-trace procambium. Similarly the first xylem and phloem appearing below the apex pertain to leaf traces. Later, when more leaves arise at the apex and the formerly youngest vascularized node or internode enters an older plastochronic stage, some of its new vascular bundles are leaf-trace sympodia (compare C with F in Figure 3-2). Thus the sympodial bundles are initiated somewhat later than the leaf traces, and since the structure of the vascular bundles is related to the over-all growth of the shoot, the leaf traces and leaf-trace sympodia differ in structure. To discuss this difference it is necessary to make a synthesis of highly fragmentary information. A study relating the differentiation of the entire primary vascular system of the shoot to the vascularization of leaves and to the developmental changes at the successively lower levels of the axis has not been made.

Therefore the description that follows may be considered as having been developed by extrapolation.

One of the differences between the bundles in a given transection of an internode is related to basipetal differentiation of the protoxylem. Several successive files of this xylem are initiated at one locus and follow one another in the basipetal course in the stem. Consequently the young leaf trace develops more protoxylem above than it does below. In the meantime the lower levels of the axis pass through successive developmental stages that, with regard to the xylem, may be called protoxylem, metaxylem, and, if present, secondary-xylem stages. At a given level in the shoot, all vascular tissue is in the same stage of development, so that if a basipetally differentiating protoxylem does not reach a given level before the metaxylem begins to differentiate, the leaf trace has metaxylem instead of protoxylem next to the pith. Most likely the trace is a part of a sympodium at this level. Thus, around the circumference of a stem, the bundles vary in the total amount of xylem and in the relative amounts of protoxylem and metaxylem.

Because of its acropetal differentiation, the phloem shows a different developmental pattern. Though at maturity xylem and phloem are usually combined into bundles, in the early differentiation of a leaf trace, phloem alone is represented. The association with the xylem develops gradually from the point of xylem initiation upward in the leaf bundle and downward in its trace. Because of the protoxylem-metaxylem relation outlined previously, the primary phloem of a given trace may become associated with metaxylem instead of protoxylem at the lower levels, or even with only secondary xylem. Thus, at lower levels the vascular bundles of a given transection of the stem show various combinations of ontogenetic stages of vascular tissues (Fig. 4-9). These are (1) bundles with protoxylem, metaxylem, metaphloem, and protophloem—leaf traces to nearest leaves; (2) bundles with a smaller amount of protoxylem—traces or trace sympodia related to higher leaves; (3) bundles with metaxylem and primary phloem, with or without protophloem; and (4) bundles with only primary phloem, which later becomes associated with secondary xylem. Another complication results when the phloem spreads far beyond the limits of the associated primary xylem, as exemplified by *Lycopersicon* (e.g., Thompson and Heimsch, 1964) or *Pelargonium* (e.g., Blyth, 1958).

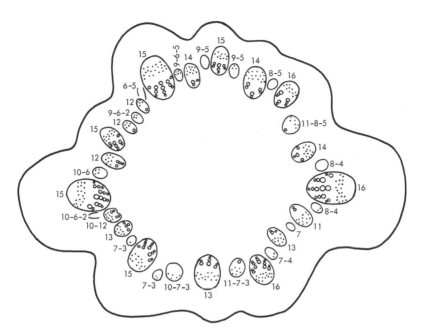

Fig. 4–9. Transverse section of *Helianthus* stem showing leaf traces (single numbers) and leaf-trace sympodia (groups of numbers). The leaves were numbered beginning with the youngest. Circles represent xylem elements; dots, sieve elements. Both representations are based on actual counts. Section 1.5 mm below apex. (After Esau [1945].)

Occurrence of phloem without xylem may lead to misconceptions regarding organization of the vascular system. Ball (1949), for example, described "interfascicular phloem" in the stem of *Lupinus*; upon closer inspection (O'Neill, 1961), this proved to be leaf-trace phloem. The Ergänzungsbündel (additional bundles), Leptombündel (phloem bundles), and interfascicular sieve tubes described by Resch (1959a) need similar reinvestigation. (The isolated sieve tubes in *Cucurbita*, Resch, 1959b, are the well-known extrafascicular sieve tubes.) It bears repeating that without a thorough knowledge of the relation of leaves to the vascular system of the shoot, based on level-by-level study of leaf-trace connections, no reliable interpretation of the entire complement of the units of the vascular system can be made.

Discontinuous xylem

In *Coleus* the xylem of a young leaf became connected with older xylem within one plastochron (Jacobs and Morrow, 1957). Thus, usually only one pair of leaves had discontinuous xylem. In a young *Helianthus* plant having ten leaves, four leaves had some xylem, and this tissue was discontinuous in two of the four (Esau, 1945). In an old plant of *Linum perenne*, some six plastochrons intervened between the appearance of xylem in a leaf and the connection of this xylem with mature xylem in the stem (Esau, 1943a).

In *Lupinus* the number of leaves with discontinuous xylem increased as the plant grew older and the number reached fifteen in a 60-day-old plant (O'Neill, 1961). This change introduced differences in the type of connection between the younger and the older xylem. The xylem of the earlier leaf traces became connected with the primary xylem, but that of the later traces (six of the fifteen in the 60-day-old plant) fused with the secondary xylem, which in the meantime was differentiating acropetally.

The discontinuous xylem is not limited to one or two longitudinal files of cells and may be associated with a considerable amount of xylem in the leaf blade (Fig. 4-8). Jacobs and Morrow (1957) point out that the leaf with discontinuous xylem in *Coleus* is morphologically complex, having a developing lamina and veins. Moreover, the leaf increases in length more than twofold between the initiation and the establishment of continuity of the xylem. The authors suggest that the procambium and the phloem are efficient in transporting materials to this leaf.

RELATION TO PHYLLOTAXIS

Relatively few authors have assembled sufficient data for a discussion of the relation between sequences in vascularization and phyllotaxis. Table 4-1 presents the most complete data available. If one adapts the concept of Priestley and his coworkers (Priestley and Scott, 1936; Priestley, Scott, and Mattinson, 1937) to the analysis of this table, one can say that in the 3 + 5 shoots, primordia contain no vascular elements for about 2 × 8 (2 × sum of contact parastichies) plastochrons, only phloem elements during the next 1 × 8 plastochrons, and xylem and phloem elements during 3 × 8 plastochrons after leaf initiation. In the 5 + 8 shoots, the corresponding numbers of plastochrons would be approximately 2 × 13, 1 × 13, and 3 × 13. Thus, the developmental events permit the arrangement of leaves in series related to phyllotaxes of the shoots. Girolami's (1953) study of *Linum usitatissimum* shows a similar trend. As indicated in Figures 2-2 and 2-3, the contact parastichy sets observed were 3 + 5, 5 + 8, and 4 + 7; the plastochronic intervals between leaf-trace connections were 5, 8, and 7 (equal the larger numbers of contact parastichies); numbers of plastochrons before phloem differentiation were 12, 16, and 15; and the numbers of plastochrons before xylem differentiation were 17, 27, and 26.

Table 4-1

Initial Vascularization in Five Vegetative Shoots of One Plant of *Linum perenne* L.

Contact parastichies	Plasto-chronic intervals between leaf-trace connections	Number of nodes in first mm of shoot	Plastochronic intervals between leaf initiation and first maturation in leaf or leaf trace		Length in microns of first leaf with mature sieve tube
			Phloem	Xylem	
3 + 5	8	36	15	22	340
3 + 5	8	40	15	21	294
5 + 8	13	64	25	39	273
5 + 8	13	56	25	39	301
5 + 8	13	64	32	48	280

(After Esau, 1943a)

In five *Helianthus* plants with leaf numbers ranging from 6 to 18, the plastochronic intervals between leaves in different stages of vascularization were higher in older plants than they were in the younger: phloem appeared in plastochrons 3 versus 5, xylem in plastochrons 5 versus 7 or 8 (Fig. 4-8). The change from younger to older plants is possibly correlated with change in phyllotaxy, since *Helianthus* is known to have a succession of leaf arrangements from decussate to ⅜. Similarly to *Linum*, *Helianthus* furnishes an indication of an increase of plastochronic intervals between developmental events with an increase in the phyllotactic fractions.

Table 4-1 shows that the leaves with the first phloem did not differ much in length. Girolami (1954) made a similar observation on *Linum usitatissimum*. The studies of Jacobs and Morrow (1957, 1958) also give evidence of close relation between size of leaves and stage of vascularization. It appears that increase in the phyllotactic value raises the plastochronic age of the leaf with the first phloem but does not affect its size. Table 4-1 indicates that this change in the plastochronic relations in the 5 + 8 shoots is associated with a greater crowding of leaves: the 3 + 5 shoots have longer internodes than the 5 + 8 shoots (Table 4-1, third column).

It is pertinent to emphasize the evidence on the difference in plastochronic age between leaves in apparently similar stages of development—and growing on the same plant—with regard to the use of the plastochron index for quantitative descriptions of leaf development (Maksymowych, 1959; Michelini, 1958). According to Michelini (1958, p. 525), the plastochron may be used as the unit of a developmental scale when successive plastochrons are of equal duration. In the *Linum* shoot under discussion, the plastochrons probably became shorter with the change of phyllotaxis from 3 + 5 to 5 + 8 contact parastichies.

Jacobs and Raghavan's studies (1962) on vascularization in *Perilla*, on the other hand, indicate that the relation between stage of vascular differentiation and length of a leaf in the same plant may also change. After the plants were exposed to inductive photoperiods, the levels of vascular differentiation changed in that maturation of the first phloem and xylem elements occurred in shorter leaves than it did during the vegetative growth. The authors relate this change to a faster initiation of leaves in photoinduced plants and they speak of speeding up of formation of vascular tissues in leaf primordia. *Perilla* has decussate leaves, hence no phyllotactic changes occurred during the different stages of shoot growth.

DIFFERENTIATION IN LEAF BLADES

Vascular differentiation in leaf blades has been given even less attention than that in the shoots. A few substantial studies deal with procambial differentiation (Chapter Three); a larger number of papers partially describe the differentiation of the xylem. The phloem has received only passing comments.

According to Scott and Priestley (1925), the first xylem of *Tradescantia* leaves differentiates acropetally in the primary longitudinal veins. The xylem in the median of these veins reaches the leaf apex first. Subsequently a group of tracheids is formed at the apex. Files of xylem elements differentiate basipetally from this group, along the margin of the blade, and eventually unite with the acropetally differentiating xylem of the lateral primary veins. The xylem of the smaller longitudinal veins and that of the transverse anastomoses differentiates basipetally. The acropetal differentiation occurs while the leaf is meristematic and is growing in length. The basipetal course is related to cessation of apical growth in the leaf. Xylem development in the leaf of *Narcissus* (Denne, 1960) resembles that in *Tradescantia*.

Sharman's (1942) study on vascularization of maize (*Zea*) leaves considers differentiation of phloem also and relates the successive events to the classification into proto and meta tissues. During the initial elongation of the leaf, protophloem and protoxylem differentiate acropetally in the median and the large lateral veins, the same veins that differentiate acropetally in the procambial stage (Chapter Three). After the elongation growth is completed, metaphloem and metaxylem differentiate basipetally in the large veins and in the small veins (these developed basipetally in the procambial stage), which thus lack protophloem and protoxylem. This interpretation once more illustrates use of the classification into proto and meta tissues with reference to a vascular system of an organ rather than to individual bundles. At a given time and at a given level of a leaf, all developing vascular bundles are of the same ontogenetic stage.

The downward wave of differentiation in the leaf of *Zea* is related to the general downward directed maturation of the leaf blade and is preceded by an intercalary elongation at the base of the leaf and leaf sheath. During this growth the protoxylem of the large veins is ruptured, an event that may occur before the basipetally differentiating metaxylem reaches that level (Sharman, 1942). Corresponding changes in the phloem need further study, although destruction of protophloem in the intercalary-growth region is known to occur. The commissural transverse connections between the longitudinal veins mature in the basipetal direction.

Xylem differentiation in the blades of dicotyledons shows somewhat varied patterns depending on the manner of growth of the leaf. In the first vein, usually the midvein, xylem differentiation is part of the initial acropetal wave of vascularization in leaves described earlier in this chapter. The development of further veins may be discussed first with reference to a specific example (*Anagallis*; Fig. 4-10; De Sloover, 1958). After the acropetally differentiating midvein xylem reaches the tip of the leaf (Fig. 4-10, A and B), lateral veins show a basipetal progress of xylem maturation, with some addition of xylem to the midvein (Fig. 4-10, C and D). The xylem of the lowermost lateral veins differentiates acropetally at a later stage of leaf development (Fig. 4-10, E). The xylem of the minor veins may mature discontinuously or at once through the entire extent of the vein. Because of the varied directions of differentiation, tracheary files in the same bundle may mature in opposite directions (Fig. 4-10, D).

In *Coleus* and *Ligustrum* (De Sloover, 1958) the lower secondary veins exhibit a continuous acropetal differentiation of xylem, and the other secondary veins have mature xylem in isolated loci at first. Bidirectional maturation, toward the principal vein and toward the leaf margin, follows. In some of these veins the entire course is acropetal beginning from the principal vein.

According to Pray (1955a), in *Liriodendron* most of the veins have a continuous progressive maturation of tracheary elements, but discontinuities in the process may occur in veins of various categories (Fig. 3-8, A). These temporary discontinuities are particularly common in the minor venation except in the vein endings. In these the tracheary elements appear first at the base of the terminal veinlet, in contact with previously differentiated xylem, and mature progressively toward the ends (Fig. 3-8, B). Xylary differentiation begins when the leaves are about one half mature but is completed after the leaf attains full size. Pray (1955a) also examined phloic differentiation in the Liriodendron leaf and found that it precedes xylary differentiation and is continuous throughout.

In the conifer *Taxus* (De Sloover, 1958) the xylem of the single vein differentiates mainly acropetally. When the xylem reaches the top of the leaf and the leaf completes its elongation at this level,

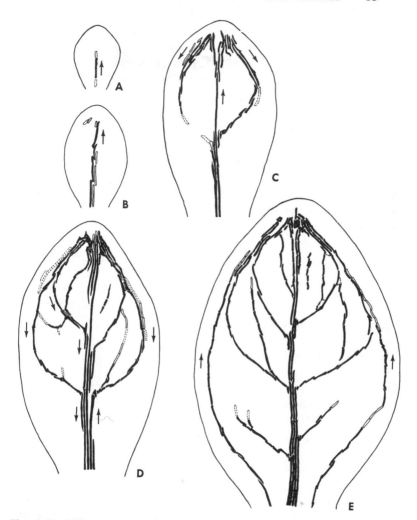

Fig. 4-10. Differentiation of xylem in leaf blades of *Anagallis arvensis;* A–E, successive stages. The first xylem of the midvein differentiates acropetally (A–C). The xylem of lateral veins in upper part of leaf differentiates basipetally (C and D); so does some additional xylem in midvein. The lower lateral veins form their xylem in acropetal direction (E). Black, mature cells. (After De Sloover [1958].)

short tracheids (presumably of the transfusion tissue) differentiate around the original bundle, with some additions in the basipetal direction.

The observations on xylem differentiation reviewed above agree in general with the classic extensive studies of Trécul (1881; see Esau, 1943c) on the same subject. Like De Sloover (1958) Trécul based his studies on cleared material.

DIFFERENTIATION IN BUDS AND FLOWERS

According to the available literature, the xylem in traces of the first leaves on the bud (prophylls) differentiates bidirectionally as it does in leaves on a shoot (De Sloover, 1958; Garrison, 1949a,b; Gifford, 1951; Marsden and Bailey, 1955). The basipetal wave brings about the connection between the bud and the main axis. Some xylem may advance acropetally from the main axis toward the bud. According to Trécul (1881), in the axillary shoots of *Primula* the acropetal element of growth occurred in less vigorous shoots but was omitted in the vigorous ones; in the weakest shoots the bidirectional element was omitted. In the limited studies on the first phloem of axillary buds this tissue was found differentiating acropetally from the main axis toward the prophylls (Esau, 1945; Garrison, 1949a,b).

With regard to reproductive shoots, procambial differentiation has received the main attention (Chapter Three). The change in speed of vascular maturation after photoinduction in *Perilla* has already been mentioned. Some studies were carried out on xylem differentiation in flowers (see Esau, 1943c). Varied patterns were observed, commonly similar to those in foliage leaves.

CONCLUSION

The statement about inadequacy of information in the conclusion to Chapter Three—procambial differentiation—can be repeated with reference to the differentiation of the primary vascular tissues in the shoot. Relatively few studies have been carried out with sufficient appreciation of the technical problems involved and with proper understanding of the relation between vascular differentiation and organization and growth of the shoot as a whole. These few studies have revealed a degree of consistency in the pattern of initiation of the first phloem and the first xylem. In general, the phloem follows the procambium in its acropetal differentiation from the stem toward the leaf primordia, whereas the xylem is initiated in positional relation to a leaf and differentiates bidirectionally, acropetally in the leaf, basipetally in the stem. Thus it appears that the development of xylem more strongly expresses the influence of the leaf on the organization of the vascular system of the shoot than does that of procambium and phloem. In terms of plastochronic timing, the phloem appears earlier than the xylem and consequently occurs closer to the apex than does the xylem. The plastochronic interval between leaf initiation and vascular maturation may be affected by shifts in phyllotactic patterns, evidence of the existence of a mechanism concerned with timing and synchronization of the physiological processes that occur in the growing shoot (Dormer, 1955b).

chapter five

➤➤➤➤ Vascularization in
Experimentally
Treated Plants

INTRODUCTION

Causal relations in growth and differentiation cannot be interpreted by observation alone. Investigators interested in origin and development of form and structure, that is, in morphogenesis, use experimental methods of study. They make the plant or plant tissue respond to specific treatments, and they interpret the results in terms of causes and effects.

Experimental work on plant development may include some of the following treatments: use of chemicals, especially growth substances of the auxin type; surgical manipulations; control of environmental factors; and culture of tissues or organs excised from plants. Experimental techniques enable one to isolate factors affecting development of certain features and to create conditions that allow the cell, tissue, or plant to duplicate at least some of the aspects of normal development in a completely analyzable environment. The results are used not only to relate certain factors to certain developmental phenomena, but also to discuss, more broadly, the meaning of patterns in plants and the probable ultimate origin of plant organization.

Experimental work with vascular plants is not necessarily directed toward problems of vascularization. But since vascular differentiation is one of the most important aspects of development of a vascular plant, it is prominently considered in discussions on morphogenesis. In this book, the experimental work on morphogenesis is reviewed only to the extent that it contributes information to causal relations in vascularization or that it uses the phenomena of vascularization to explain the results obtained.

A meaningful interpretation of experimental results presupposes a thorough understanding of the normal development of the plant under study. As has been pointed out in the preceding two chapters, many gaps still exist in our knowledge of the development of plants, especially with regard to vascularization. In the following discussions, the conclusions drawn from studies on morphogenesis are evaluated in relation to the quantity and quality of information available on the normal structure and development of the experimental plants.

EFFECT OF REMOVAL OF LEAVES

Experiments involving removal of leaf primordia or prevention of development of such primordia by destruction (for example, by puncturing) of sites of future primordia are usually designed to test the possible relation between the development of leaf traces and the origin of leaves. In one of the earliest experiments of this type —one that is much quoted in the literature on morphogenesis— Helm (1932), using shoots of dicotyledons, removed leaf primordia which were just individualized (*abgegliedert*) or were becoming so (*in Abgliederung begriffen*) and let the plants grow for some time before he examined the anatomic results of the operation. Sometimes the primordium was removed in toto, sometimes a stump was left. Thus, Helm had removed visible primordia which, according to our present knowledge on vascularization of vegetative shoots (Chapter Three), may be assumed to have had leaf traces, at least in procambial state. Indeed, Helm was observing alterations in existing leaf traces. The upper younger parts of these traces were affected most; the procambium had differentiated into parenchyma instead of vascular tissues. The effect decreased basipetally but could extend two to three internodes below the site of operation. Helm's statement that new traces were not formed is misleading. He was carrying out his experiments at the time when basipetal differentiation of procambium from leaf primordia through the stem was assumed to be the established pattern (see Esau, 1943c). If he were aware of the other possibility, he might have said that no basipetal differentiation of traces from the injured leaf sites had occurred.

Several other experiments involving removal of leaf primordia in dicotyledons yielded results similar to those of Helm (see Allsopp, 1964). But with ferns this type of experimentation was carried further, mainly by Wardlaw (1944, 1946a,b). Young leaves were removed from a rhizome apex, and a series of successively appearing leaf primordia were punctured. Treated and untreated portions of rhizomes were sectioned several weeks after the final puncturing. In *Dryopteris* the vascular cylinder in the untreated portions contained the usual interruptions in the form of leaf gaps (dictyostelic structure), whereas in the treated portions no gaps were present (siphonostelic structure). Similar differences were observed in other ferns. In some the treated portion of the rhizome was attenuated, and correspondingly the diameters of the vascular cylinder and the pith were reduced.

In another type of experiment (Wardlaw, 1950), destruction of certain leaf primordia induced differentiation of primordia in positions where normally they would not have appeared. A related change in the position of leaf traces was observed after the leaves in the new positions had grown for some time.

These examples of experiments on suppression of leaf growth clearly show that in ferns and seed plants the usual form of the vascular system of shoots is determined by the interaction between leaf and stem. If leaves are developing, connections with these leaves are formed in the vascular system of the stem. If leaf development is suppressed, the vascular pattern in the stem is reminiscent of the patterns found in plant axes on which leaves are relatively minor appendages not associated with gaps, or are absent (microphyllous plants, certain water plants, many rhizomes, corms, scapes, inflorescence axes, and roots).

The effect of starvation resulting from the suppression of leaf development cannot be ignored in the interpretation of the defoliation experiments. According to West (1917), for example, the vascular system of the adult axis of an ill-nourished specimen of the fern *Danaea* resembled that of a young sporophyte in which gaps and pith are normally absent. By removing the cotyledons in seedlings of *Vicia* and *Phaseolus*, Flaskämper (1910) obtained reduction and sometimes complete suppression of pith in the taproot portion that developed soon after the operation. With further growth of the seedling, normal structure appeared in the newly developing root portion.

Students of morphogenesis find deeper implications in the effects of defoliation than those given above (see Wetmore and Wardlaw, 1951). They interpret the change from presence to absence of gaps as fundamental in nature and as proof that the vascular system of the axis is truly cauline rather than a composite of leaf traces. The manifest artificiality of the distinction between the cauline vascular tissue and the leaf traces has been emphasized before (Chapter One; see also Allsopp, 1964, and Clowes, 1961) and need not be further discussed. But reference should be made here once more to the hypothetical concept of the incipient vascular tissue of Wardlaw (Chapter Three), a concept used in interpreting the results of leaf-removal experiments. Prevention of development of leaves is supposed to eliminate the "breaking" of the initially continuous incipient vascular tissue by leaf gaps (Wetmore and Wardlaw, 1951). In his studies of shoot apices of several leptosporangiate ferns Hagemann (1964) was unable to detect any potential vascular tissue in the distal region of the shoot other than the discrete procambial leaf traces associated with the youngest leaf primordia. Hagemann's illustrations and conclusions support the contention of Esau (1954, p. 52) that Wardlaw's incipient vascular tissue is pith meristem that has certain resemblance to the youngest procambium: shallow, relatively chromophilic cells arranged in series. These characteristics are also those of a rib meristem, a common growth form of a young pith.

DETERMINATION OF SITES OF LEAVES

The relation between leaf traces and leaves does not play a large part in discussions on causal factors in leaf arrangement. In the English-language literature the popular explanation of this arrangement is made in terms of space in the apical meristem and the shape of apex and leaf primordia (see Clowes, 1961). In France, on the other hand, the prevailing concept states that a leaf-forming impulse moves upward along foliar parastichies toward their termination in leaf generative centers near the apex (see Cutter, 1959, and Loiseau, 1959).

Students of vascularization, however, have expressed views on possible significance of acropetal differentiation of procambium in determination of leaf sites. Several authors have suggested that the differentiation of a procambial strand toward the shoot apex determines the position of the future leaf especially if this strand is discernible before the leaf to which it pertains is initiated (e.g., Gunckel and Wetmore, 1946a; Smith, 1941; Sterling, 1945). This suggestion stimulated much research intended to test the hypothesis. The principal method used consisted of undercutting those regions of the apical meristem where new leaves were expected to arise (Snow and Snow, 1947, 1948; Wardlaw, 1949a, 1956; see also Allsopp, 1964). The operations did not prevent leaves from developing, so the conclusion was drawn that the position of leaf primordia was not determined by the differentiating leaf traces.

Accurate observations on procambial differentiation in the treated plants or their controls were not included in the studies on leaf-site determination just reviewed. According to Wardlaw (1956), in the ferns "precocious leaf traces" were not observed in the experimental plants. At the same time, Wardlaw pictures the previously mentioned incipient vascular tissue—also termed procambium (Wardlaw, 1949b, 1952)—as underlying the prospective leaf sites and reports that the severance of this tissue causes important changes in the activity of the apex (Wardlaw, 1956; Wardlaw and Cutter, 1956). Criteria for distinguishing the "precocious leaf traces" from the "incipient vascular tissue" located beneath the apex with its potential leaf sites are not given.

The whole inquiry as to whether procambial differentiation determines leaf sites or whether, conversely, leaf primordia induce differentiation of their traces (Ball, 1949) seems to be based on too narrow a conception of a highly complex problem of plant organization. Initiation of leaves and differentiation of procambium in positional relations to leaves are two of many synchronized phenomena occurring in a growing shoot. As Philipson (1949) has suitably stated, the two phenomena are complementary aspects of one process.

EFFECTS OF PARTIAL ISOLATION AND DIVISION
OF APEX

Students of morphogenesis try to determine whether the shoot apex is an autonomous center of organization—except that it receives nutrients from below—or is directed by the differentiated tissues. Some of the prominent tests of these alternative hypotheses have been based on microsurgery: isolation of the apex from the adjoining tissues by vertical cuts, division of apices by similar cuts, and culture of completely isolated apices (see Allsopp, 1964). Such experiments indicate the ability of the apex to continue growth. Partly isolated apices eventually developed into vascularized shoots and formed a vascular connection with subjacent parts of the axis. Divided apices produced multiple vascularized shoots. Cultured apices formed roots and finally developed into complete plants; in angiosperms, however, this occurred only when the initially isolated apex was associated with a few leaf primordia (Allsopp, 1964).

Ball (1952a) provided some details on the establishment of procambial connection of the partly isolated apex with the stem below. After the operation, which was made as close as possible to the apex so as to exclude all leaf primordia, the meristem was supported by a plug of pith parenchyma (Fig. 5-1, A). No vascular connection in any stage of development was present between the meristem and the mature tissues. The space between the plug and the laterally adjacent tissue became filled with callus tissue, the apical meristem initiated some leaf primordia, and a procambial connection with the older tissue developed basipetally through the pith (Fig. 5-1, B). Thus, the regenerated shoot became connected with the older part of the shoot according to the pattern previously described for adventitious buds and those axillary buds that become separated from the vascular system of the main shoot by vacuolated parenchyma. As discussed in Chapter Three, the procambium of such buds differentiates basipetally toward the main axis. In ferns, the regenerated shoots resembled buds that may be induced in relatively mature parts of the rhizome (Wardlaw, 1947). The basipetally differentiating strands of procambium ended before reaching the main vascular system.

Studies on vascularization of shoots regenerated from partly

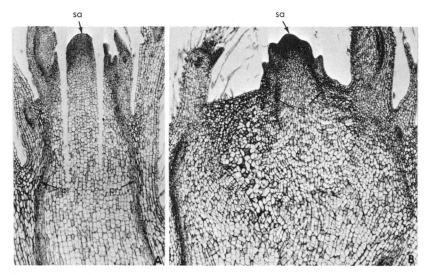

Fig. 5–1. Longitudinal sections of *Lupinus* shoot. (*A*) Immediately after the operation isolating the apical meristem (*sa*) by four longitudinal cuts. The isolated column of tissue is approximately 800 μ long. (*B*) Fourteen days after operation. The shoot apex (*sa*) has become elevated by elongation of subadjacent tissue, the cuts have been filled with wound-healing tissue, and the apex has initiated some leaves and has formed some procambium (*pr*) differentiating basipetally. Both × 45. (From Ball [1952a].)

isolated apices would have been much more informative if they had included a complete ontogenetic study relating procambial differentiation to the emergence of leaf primordia. In axillary buds the first procambial strands are prophyll traces (Chapter Three). This relation prevails whether the procambium of the bud differentiates acropetally (Garrison, 1949a,b) or basipetally (Gifford, 1951). Longitudinal sections of regenerated shoots suggest a connection of the basipetally differentiating procambium with the leaf primordia (Fig. 5-1, B). Ball (1952a), however, states that the prospective vascular tissue appeared first as a tube. Whether this tube consisted of procambium or a residual type of meristem is not clear (see Esau, 1954). Subsequently the usual organization into strands (probably leaf traces and their sympodia) was present.

In shoot apices divided by vertical cuts (e.g., Ball, 1952b) the segments that were not too small grew into independent shoots comparable to the original. Since each segment maintained lateral continuity with the shoot below, the vascular tissue developed partly in normal position, partly basipetally along the incisions from tissue that would have formed the pith.

Well-developed regenerated shoots had cylinders of bundles in later stages of growth. The union below of the two or more cylinders of the regenerated shoots was morphologically similar to a union of a branch and a stem when the two do not greatly differ in size.

The results of partial isolation and dissection of shoot apices were interpreted as suggesting, first, that formation of new vascular tissue is induced by the apex and, second, that the form of the initial vascular tissue (rod or tube) proves the existence of cauline vascular tissue independent of leaf traces.

The first conclusion, that the apex rather than the tissues below determine the appearance of vascular tissue, is based on the occurrence of basipetal differentiation of procambium in regenerated shoots (see Allsopp, 1964). As mentioned before, basipetal procambial differentiation occurs also during the establishment of connection of adventitious and certain axillary buds with the parent shoot, but subsequent differentiation of the procambium in shoots derived from the buds is acropetal. One can assume that the same pattern prevails in regenerated shoots (no reliable information is available on this point), and therefore apical activity must be interpreted in terms of both basipetal and acropetal procambial differentiation. It also is important to know whether the initial connection of the regenerated shoot with the parent axis occurs in relation to the first leaves as it does in an axillary bud; that is, whether the induction comes from the apex itself or from a shoot with growing primordia.

It is pertinent to mention here the significant observation of Gulline (1960) that the basipetal differentiation of procambium from an adventitious bud is strictly polar. Buds were induced to form on portions of epidermal tissue grafted in inverted position on hypocotyls of flax. In the inverted bud, the vascular tissue developed basipetally with regard to the bud, that is, upward with reference to the hypocotyl. But in the hypocotyl itself, the course was sharply reversed to a basipetal one with respect to the hypocotyl axis.

With regard to the second conclusion, that part of the vascular tissue of the stem is not related to leaves, the lack of meaning in a distinction between cauline tissue and leaf traces has been amply discussed. But it should be pointed out that the second conclusion was derived from an inadequate analysis of both the normal and the experimentally treated shoots (see Esau, 1954).

VASCULAR DIFFERENTIATION IN TISSUE CULTURES

Callus tissue obtained in cultures beginning with undifferentiated parenchymatic explants may spontaneously develop vascular tissue. Commonly such vascular tissue is not organized into a system but occurs as nodules or short strands composed of xylem alone or of xylem and phloem (Ball, 1950; Gautheret, 1959). Cambium may be present between the two tissues. In many tissue-culture experiments the callus growth is obtained from the parenchyma of secondary vascular tissues, particularly the phloem, of fleshy roots. If the explant is xylem tissue, the xylem of vascular units in the callus is oriented toward the original explant; if the explant is phloem tissue, the phloem of nodules in the callus is turned toward the explant. Gautheret (1959) suggests that the explants establish gradients of differentiation.

Investigators have learned to dissociate callus tissue (chiefly that obtained from carrot root) into individual cells, and these workers are studying differentiation in growths derived from single cells (Steward et al., 1958). While the aggregates derived from a single cell are small, the component cells are parenchymatic. When the aggregate attains a certain size—supposedly sufficiently large to remove the center from the direct effect of the medium—xylem develops in the center (Fig. 5-2, A). The xylem becomes surrounded by cambium, and phloem elements differentiate among the cambial derivatives produced away from the xylem (Fig. 5-2, B). Eventually a root apex is formed in the cambium and develops into a root, which grows out through the tissue into the medium. With further development of the root, growth of the original nodule of tissue is retarded or suppressed. If a rooted nodule is transplanted to a certain kind of medium, it often forms a bud and regenerates a complete plant with shoot and root in vascular continuity. (The ontogenetic establishment of this continuity was not studied.)

Bud development in callus may occur before root formation

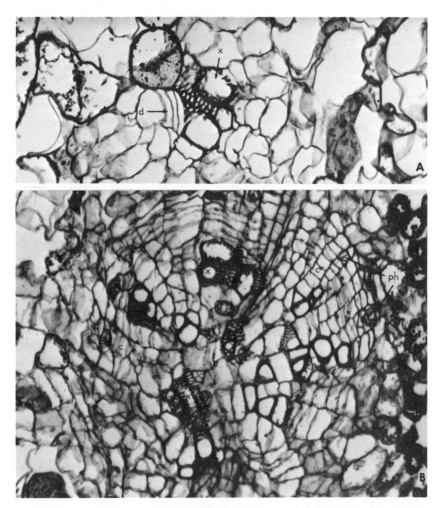

Fig. 5–2. Two stages of development of nodule from cultured, suspended cells derived from carrot-root tissue explants. (*A*) Xylem cells (*x*) differentiated within a nodule of cells. Cell division (*d*) has occurred next to them. (*B*) Later stage in vascular differentiation in a nodule. Xylem in the center surrounded by cambium (*c*). Some phloem elements (*ph*) have differentiated among the cambial products. Both × 330. (From Steward *et al.* [1958].)

or without it. Ball (1950), for example, obtained buds in callus cultures in *Sequoia sempervirens*, but apparently no roots. Camus (1949) observed spontaneously developing buds on cultured fragments of endive roots and later differentiation of conducting elements in subjacent tissue directed from the bud toward the cambium of the explant. Beneath the union of the new vascular tissue with the cambium the latter proliferated and formed vascular elements. If the experimental material was capable of producing roots in vitro, the rhizogenesis occurred in line with the vascular differentiation directed from the bud. Thus, according to Camus (1949), vascular differentiation is polarized in the direction from the leafy shoot toward the root.

Camus (1949) found also that buds grafted on cultured fragments of endive roots induce vascular differentiation in the subjacent callus. If buds were grafted into the phloem of the root explant, vascular strands oriented toward the cambium were obtained. If the grafting was done into xylem parenchyma, only randomly arranged isolated units of vascular tissue developed under the influence of the bud. Camus obtained evidence that induction of vascular tissue by the bud is hormonal in nature. Induction occurred when the bud was separated from the callus by a membrane, and application of auxin to the callus had an effect similar to that produced by bud grafting.

Wetmore and his associates (Wetmore and Sorokin, 1955; Wetmore and Rier, 1963) further refined the study of the bud effect on callus. First, they succeeded in culturing completely undifferentiated parenchymatic callus from several species of dicotyledons (chiefly *Syringa*). Then they induced in such callus distinctive, reproducible patterns of vascularization by means of bud grafts or auxins substituting for the buds. They also learned to vary the composition of the induced vascular tissue by altering the concentrations of applied auxins and sugar.

When the bud grafted into the callus started growing, scattered nodules of dividing cells appeared near the lower end of the bud along its sides. The nodules differentiated into vascular tissue. Deeper in the callus, nodules developed in a circular arrangement, with the xylem directed toward the center of the circle, the phloem away from it. In later stages cambium was frequently present within the nodules and even between the bundles if these were close together. In this manner, a considerable degree of continuity was established in the circle. Additional nodules differentiated in the deeper part of the callus, which was immersed in the medium.

Here the nodules occurred in scattered distribution near the periphery but with the phloem turned toward the medium. The entire pattern of vascularization of the callus was reproducible by a substitution of the graft by agar containing a certain concentration of indoleacetic acid and sucrose. It appears, therefore, that hormones are primary factors in vascular differentiation in the callus, and that in the induction of such differentiation by the bud the latter is the source of hormones.

The results of these experiments are interpreted as supporting the concept of basipetal induction of vascular tissue by the apex or apical meristem (Allsopp, 1964; Wetmore and Rier, 1963). It is not certain whether the authors refer to the apical meristem specifically, that is, to the meristem located above the youngest leaf primordium. According to Wetmore and Rier (1963), the scion that was effective in inducing cell division and vascular differentiation in the callus had leaves that were opening and developing. In fact, in all grafting experiments involving callus, shoot tips with leaf primordia ("buds") rather than apices alone were implanted. That is, the callus was supplied not with apical meristems but with organized shoots. In view of the controversies regarding the exact role of the apical meristem as such in the edification of the shoot (see Clowes, 1961), this distinction cannot be ignored.

Wetmore and Rier (1963) find that the distribution of nodules in the callus suggests an induction of centers of mitotic activity on diffusion gradients related to definite concentrations of diffusing substances. The circular arrangement of the nodules indicates that the diffusion gradients are established symmetrically, possibly in agreement with the radial symmetry of the shoot. If several buds were grafted close together in a circle, the nodules differentiated in a single circle; more widely spaced buds induced individual circles. Circular arrangement of nodules was obtained also when the incision for the bud was filled with auxin-containing agar. When the auxin and sugar were applied in a solution through a micropipette inserted in the callus, a complete ring of xylem and phloem with a cambium between them was formed around the pipette. The authors call attention to the similarity between these patterns and those characteristic of the vascular system of many stems and roots. They look toward an eventual interpretation of stelar patterns on the basis of concentrations and distributions of auxins and sugars.

The role of hormonal stimulus in differentiation of vascular tissues should be explored with regard to the variations in the direction of normal procambial differentiation, acropetal in some instances, basipetal in others. During the continuous, completely synchronized differentiation in the vegetative shoot of a dicotyledon or gymnosperm, the inductive factor can be visualized as carried upward with the continuous elevation of the shoot tip. In the monocotyledons the relatively strongly expressed intercalary elongation of stems and leaves may alter the pattern of induction and bring about a basipetal differentiation of procambium, particularly in those leaf traces of a given leaf that are formed after the elongation of the internode has begun. In an axillary or adventitious bud, which is separated by vacuolated tissue from the vascular system of the parent shoot, or in the adventitious bud in the root-fragment culture of Camus (1949), the induction comes from the growing bud and results in a basipetal differentiation of the connection with preexisting tissues. If the inductive impulse is propagated in an undifferentiated callus, as in Wetmore and Rier's experiments, no continuous vascular tissue arises. Conceivably, if roots were present in the callus tissue, as in the cultures of Steward et al. (1958), a continuous basipetal vascular differentiation would occur through the callus. One can visualize the developmental patterns as depending on the presence of inductive factors and on the nature and the condition of the plant part in which induction occurs.

POSITIONAL RELATION OF XYLEM AND PHLOEM

One of the important unexplained features in vascular differentiation is the common position of xylem and phloem—the xylem directed toward the center of the axis and the phloem toward its periphery—in both primary and secondary vascular systems. Exceptions, such as those found among plants with anomalous growth and those with internal phloem, make the explanation of the common pattern even more difficult.

Steward et al. (1958) propose a biochemical interpretation of the distribution of xylem and phloem in the concentric nodules found in their callus cultures (Fig. 5-2, B), as follows: Cell aggregate reaches a size that creates a modified environment for the inner cells and they behave differently from the outer. The inner cells become tracheids and lose their contents. Cambial cells develop about these lignified elements as if they were responding to injury. The dividing cells in this cambium lie along a gradient from the dead cells within to the nutrient without. Thus the phloem differentiates in a different nutritional condition than the xylem, perhaps one related to a balance between sugar and auxin. General applicability of this interpretation may be questioned, however, because it would not explain the origin of bundles (amphivasal bundles) in which the xylem encloses a centrally located phloem. These bundles are found in some dicotyledons and monocotyledons.

Gradient effects are sometimes mentioned also in discussions of the position of the vascular cambium in normal growth. Earlier workers assumed that the cambium forms beneath a natural or an artificial free surface and produces phloem outwards and xylem inwards. On the basis of regeneration phenomena in wounded solanaceous stems, the Warren Wilsons (1961) propose that a gradient of some factor is established perpendicular to the exposed surface, and where this factor is at the appropriate level cambium is formed. They find that the gradient concept explains also situations when the positions of the phloem and xylem are reversed. In their material, for example, a reversed gradient occurs between the internal phloem and the xylem. The Warren Wilsons further propose that the direction of the gradient determines the direction in which phloem and xylem are formed. Under this concept one must assume a periodic reversal of the gradient if some phloem becomes included in the xylem as is characteristic of certain lianas with anomalous secondary growth.

Figure 5-3 illustrates the formation of cambium near a new surface, as well as a reversal of the phloem and xylem positions. A natural split occurred in the stem of *Euphrasia* and exposed the pith. A cambium developed under the new free surface and produced phloem and xylem in normal orientation with regard to this surface (Rüdiger, 1953). The cambial activity in the exposed pith apparently was propagated for some distance into the intact pith below the split and caused here the formation of xylem and ohloem in an orientation opposite to the normal.

Brown and Sax (1962) have explored the effect of physical

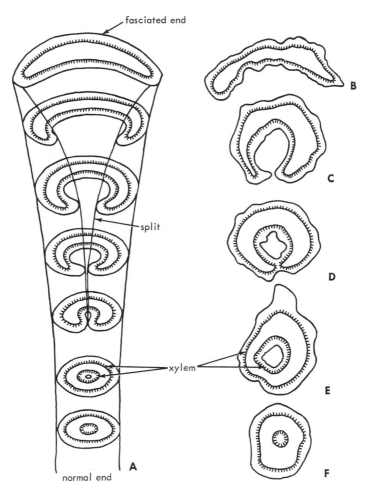

Fig. 5–3. Structure of a partly fasciated stem of *Euphrasia Odonites*. The fasciation developed in relation to a longitudinal split in the axis. (*A*) Longitudinal diagram interpreting the relation of the cross sections *B–F* to one another. Sections *B–F* are drawn from photomicrographs. (Adapted from Rüdiger [1953].)

pressure on the differentiation of the secondary vascular tissues. Longitudinal strips of bark of *Populus trichocarpa* and *Pinus strobus* stems were partly separated from the wood of the trunk and kept humid. The cambium along the inner surface of the strips proliferated into callus. A phellogen and a vascular cambium arose in this callus and transformed the free bark strip into a stemlike structure. If, however, the free bark strip was separated from the wood by a plastic film but held firmly against it by outside pressure, the cambium continued to function normally. The study was carried further by the use of tissue cultures. Inner phloem and cambium explants from stems of *Populus deltoides* proliferated and formed parenchymatic callus. When pressure was applied to the cultured tissue, parenchymatic proliferation was inhibited and a more normal pattern of differentiation was obtained (Brown, 1964).

GROWTH SUBSTANCES IN VASCULAR DIFFERENTIATION

Xylem

It has been indicated earlier in this chapter and will be again pointed out in Chapter Six that many morphogenetic studies provide evidence of hormonal control in vascular differentiation. Some research deals specifically with the effect of auxin on xylem differentiation by reference to regeneration of xylem after wounding. Such regeneration may be induced readily by breaking the continuity of an existing xylem strand. New xylem—wound xylem according to Roberts and Fosket (1962)—differentiates in parenchyma adjacent to the discontinuity and reestablishes the connection between the two parts of the severed strand. In Figure 5-4, A, the strand of normal vessels to the left was ruptured by two punctures with a microneedle made of glass; to the right appears the regenerated xylem connection. The origin of the xylem elements from parenchyma is indicated by their short lengths (Fig. 5-4, B).

Jacobs (1952, 1954) has demonstrated that in *Coleus* the auxin from developing leaves is the normal limiting factor for the differentiation of xylem during regeneration. No regeneration occurs if the leaf and the axillary bud located above the wound are removed, but it does occur if the leaf stump is covered with lanolin containing auxin. Quantitatively, a relationship exists between the amount of xylem regenerated and the amount of diffusible auxin, that is, the amount transported by the stem rather than the amount produced by the leaves. Moreover, regeneration of the xylem is polar in relation to the polarity of auxin movement (Jacobs, 1952).

Jacobs and Morrow (1957) found that normal xylem differen-

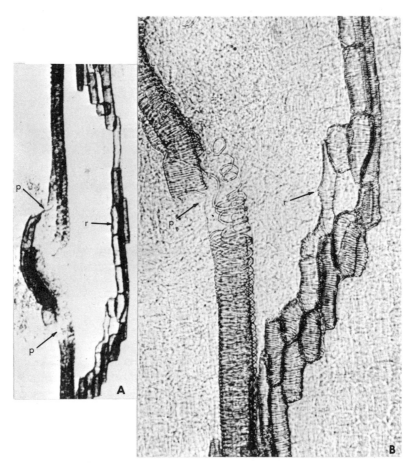

Fig. 5–4. Xylem regeneration in wounded stems of *Coleus blumei*. Lower (*A*) and higher (*B*) magnification of xylem strand broken by punctures (*p*) and regenerated (*r*) by a bridge of wound xylem. *A*, × 70; *B*, × 170. (From Roberts and Fosket [1962].)

tiation is also limited by auxin, and they attempted a quantitative comparison of auxin-xylem relations in normal and regenerative development. They calculated that the same amount of auxin acting during a specified period of time can induce ten times as many xylem cells to develop normally from procambium than to regenerate from parenchyma. Jacobs and Morrow concluded that this difference explains why parenchyma does not differentiate into xylem unless xylem is severed and the auxin reaches a high enough concentration in the parenchyma.

Jacobs (1952) considered the commonly discontinuous xylem initiation at the base of leaves in terms of a balance between auxin and sugar. He suggested that the prospective xylem cells near a leaf have sufficient auxin derived from that leaf but are limited by the sugar being transported from below by the sieve tubes; correspondingly, it has been often observed that xylem differentiation at the leaf base begins after the acropetal phloem differentiation reaches this level (Fig. 4-7). The prospective xylem below the leaf base is nearer the supply of sugar from the older leaves but farther from the auxin supplied by the young leaves above. Thus its differentiation is limited by the basipetally moving auxin. One can assume that the characteristics of auxin transport show variations in different species; concomitantly patterns of differentiation would vary.

Roberts and Fosket (1962) found that whereas in vegetative shoots of *Coleus* the wound xylem was oriented parallel to the plant axis (Fig. 5-4), in flowering stalks it formed a branching network apparently not related to the orientation of the axis. This irregularity resembled that obtained during regeneration in wounded excised vegetative shoots of *Coleus* in which the distal leaves and axillary buds were removed (Roberts, 1960). The authors suggest that in flowering and excised shoots only a low concentration of auxin was moving toward the wound site. Auxin was found to be a limiting factor in xylem regeneration in isolated stem segments of *Coleus* cultivated in vitro (Fosket and Roberts, 1964). The importance of polar transport of auxin was also recorded in these experiments.

The results on induction of vascular tissues in callus show that xylem differentiation may be induced in parenchyma without wounding the normal xylem. Clutter's (1960) experiments made another contribution to this aspect of xylem differentiation. Indoleacetic acid was added through an inserted pipette to cultured pith of *Nicotiana tabacum*. Tracheids in a haphazard arrangement or in occasional spherical groups differentiated in the pith. Then, De Maggio, Wetmore, and Morel (1963) succeeded in inducing xylem differentiation in the prothallus of the fern *Todea barbara*. Although the adult sporophyte of a fern is consistently vascularized, the prothallus of *Todea* has not been found to have xylem in normal growing conditions. A certain balance of sugar and naphthylacetic acid added to the culture medium resulted in mitotic activity and formation of nodules of tracheids in all parts of the prothallus.

An enhancement of normal xylem differentiation was obtained by Sargent and Wangermann (1959) in *Lemna minor* by addition of tri-iodo-benzoic acid to the culture solution. A more elaborate venation developed in the treated fronds. Kiermayer (1959) observed a marked increase in the development of internodal xylem by applying gibberellic acid to young leaves of *Solanum nigrum*.

Phloem

Factors involved in phloem differentiation are also beginning to be discovered. The first indication of hormonal effects in this aspect of vascularization is seen in the results of Kaan-Albest's (1934) study on phloem regeneration, chiefly in *Impatiens*. She found that removal of a certain number of leaves and buds, especially of those located upward from the wound site, reduced phloem regeneration; that phloem regeneration progressed in basipetal direction; and that stem cuttings made in the fall did not develop roots and did not regenerate phloem, whereas those made in the spring did both. According to LaMotte and Jacobs (1963), these results suggest limitation of phloem regeneration by availability of auxin from leaves and buds.

LaMotte and Jacobs (1963) found strong evidence of hormonal relations in phloem differentiation, especially in that the role of shoot organs could be carried out by applied auxins, and they observed that the auxin effect in phloem regeneration may be a direct one. A relationship existed between the number of phloem strands cut in wounding and the extent of phloem regeneration, possibly because a substance leaking from the phloem was involved in regeneration. Certain anomalies in wall differentiation were interpreted as an indication that sugars may become limiting in phloem differentiation.

Wetmore and Rier (1963) contributed to the clarification of sugar requirement in phloem differentiation. They found, in the previously reviewed experiments with callus tissue, that both auxin and sugar are necessary for the induction and completion of differentiation of xylem and phloem, but that lower concentrations of sugar favor xylem differentiation and higher concentrations favor phloem differentiation. Middle concentrations induce normal xylem and phloem development, usually with a cambium between the two.

CONCLUSION

Experimental work on various aspects of shoot morphogenesis has provided considerable information on induction and differentiation of vascular tissues. The evidence on the degree of hormonal participation in these phenomena and on the importance of a balance of auxin and sugar in the determination of the xylem and phloem content of the vascular tissues is particularly impressive. Experiments involving prevention of leaf development on shoots have provided evidence supporting the concept that in megaphyllous plants the leaves strongly influence the pattern of differentiation of the vascular system in the stem. Surgical isolation of apices created conditions resembling those prevailing in the development of adventitious buds: regenerated shoots established a vascular connection with the stem below by a basipetal differentiation of procambium. Basipetal influence of buds on subjacent tissues was observed also when buds grafted on undifferentiated callus induced the formation of nodules of vascular tissue in this callus. Since the bud could be completely replaced by a source of auxin, the basipetal induction of vascularization by the bud was related to auxin. The induction in callus consisted of cell division followed by differentiation of vascular elements. Some features of the induced tissues duplicated those found in vascular tissues in normally developing plants. Conclusions that in the experiments with buds vascularization was determined by the apical meristem should be qualified because buds with leaves were used as scions. It has been shown repeatedly that young leaves are the main source of auxins in shoots. Experiments on xylem and phloem regeneration are particularly effective in demonstrating the role of leaves as a source of auxins that induce differentiation of vascular elements.

chapter six

Vascularization
of Roots, Embryos,
and Seedlings

VASCULAR DIFFERENTIATION IN ROOTS

The vascular system of the root appears as a column in which phloem and xylem alternate around the circumference (see Fig. 6-9, C). The primary xylem often forms a solid central core, in the seed plants commonly with two or more ridgelike projections toward the periphery. These ridges alternate with the phloem strands. If pith is present, the primary xylem appears as strands corresponding to the ridges of a xylem with a solid core. The number of xylem strands or ridges varies, and the patterns are accordingly referred to as diarch (2), triarch (3), tetrarch (4), and so forth, depending on that number.

The vascular cylinder of a root is usually clearly delimited from the ground tissue, for the innermost layer of the cortex is morphologically differentiated as an endodermis—it has casparian strips or other wall thickenings—and inside of the endodermis is a continuous uniseriate, biseriate, or multiseriate tissue region, the pericycle. The root pericycle received its name after the peripheral region of the vascular system in the stem became known as the pericycle. The use of this term for the root is more acceptable than it is for the stem (Chapter One), for the root pericycle commonly includes no vascular elements. The root pericycle is sometimes called pericambium, especially in the German literature, a term which emphasizes the meristematic potentialities of the pericycle (formation of lateral roots and portions of the vascular cambium).

Descriptions of vascular differentiation in roots are commonly simplified by giving the name of procambium to the entire central column, including the future pericycle (*pr* in Fig. 6-1, A). The potential pith, if present, may be excluded under the name of ground meristem. Depending on the structure of the apical meristem, the procambial cylinder may or may not be delimited from the future cortex in the region of the apical meristem (see Clowes, 1961). It is so delimited in Figure 6-1, A. Farther from the apex, the cylinder is typically distinct from the cortex because the two tissue regions do not contribute cells to one another. It may be recalled that in the shoot, the vascular region and the cortex cannot be sharply separated during primary growth.

Latitudinal course of differentiation

In the root, both the first xylem and the first phloem elements mature next to the pericycle (Fig. 6-1), whereas the subsequent elements differentiate in successively deeper positions within the procambium. Thus, both tissues develop centripetally. The loci of the first vascular elements, as seen in transections, are commonly called protophloem and protoxylem poles for descriptive convenience. (In the three-dimensional aspect, the terms "poles" are hardly suitable.) In the diarch root depicted in Figure 6-1, there are two protophloem and two protoxylem poles. As in the shoot, the distinction between the proto and the meta tissues is often obscure because of the gradual transition from one developmental stage to the other. Therefore the delimitation between the two is drawn somewhat arbitrarily. In the roots, the number of elements that could appropriately be called protophloem and protoxylem is generally small; sometimes only one element at each pole (as seen in transections) can be assigned to these tissues. In other roots, whole groups of earliest elements at each pole appear to form ontogenetic units and are classified as protophloem and protoxylem. In the gymnosperms, for example, the earliest phloem, the so-called precursory phloem (see Wilcox, 1954, 1962a) consists of a number of cells. In the xylem of these plants, also, several tracheary elements may be conveniently interpreted as protoxylem on the basis of position and size differences from the succeeding xylem elements (Fig. 6-2). In the monocotyledons, one can commonly distinguish between the narrow protoxylem cells, the somewhat wider early metaxylem cells, and the widest late metaxylem cells, a division that proved most useful

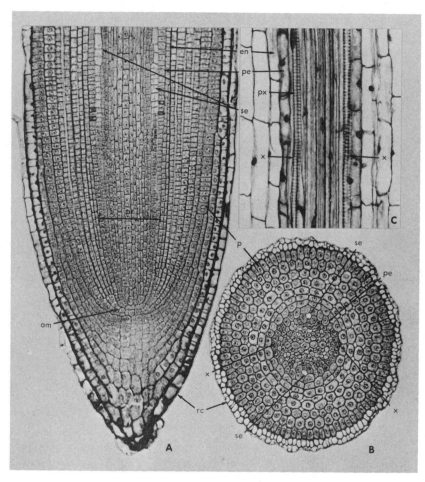

Fig. 6–1. Initial vascular differentiation in roots. Longitudinal (*A*) and transverse (*B*) sections of tomato root. (*C*) Longitudinal section of tobacco root at level of protoxylem (*px*) differentiation. (*A*) Section parallel with the phloem poles (*se* in *B*). (*C*) Section parallel with the xylem poles (*x* in *B*, *C*). Details: *am*, apical meristem; *en*, endodermis; *p*, protoderm; *pe*, pericycle; *pr*, procambium; *px*, protoxylem; *rc*, rootcap; *se*, sieve elements of protophloem; *x*, xylem poles. No mature xylem in *A* or *B*. *A* and *B*, × 190; *C*, × 180. (*A* and *B*, from Heimsch [1960].)

110

in comparative studies with reference to xylem phylogeny (Cheadle, 1953).

Figures 6-2 and 6-3 may serve for outlining the latitudinal sequence of primary xylem differentiation. These figures depict transectional views of roots of *Pinus* in which the protoxylem (*px*) appears forked; a resin duct is enclosed between the prongs of the fork (Wilcox, 1964). As mentioned in the evaluation of the terms protoxylem and metaxylem in Chapter Four, the root xylem typifies exarch xylem, that is, xylem with the protoxylem occupying the peripheral position in the vascular cylinder. This feature is clearly shown in Figure 6-2.

The appearance of the secondary walls of the first protoxylem elements (Fig. 6-2, A) occurs roughly at the level where casparian strips differentiate in the endodermis (Fig. 6-2, A, *en*) and the root hairs of the epidermis become elongated. Figure 6-2, B, indicates the first step in the centripetal maturation of the protoxylem, and in Figure 6-2, C, protoxylem maturation is completed. Inward from the protoxylem, in continuation of centripetal maturation of the primary xylem, metaxylem elements appear (Fig. 6-2, D, *mx*). Their diameters are somewhat greater than those of the protoxylem elements. Before the maturation of metaxylem reaches the center of the root, some secondary xylem is formed by the cambium which occurs on two sides of the xylem plate (Fig. 6-2, D, *sx*). Metaxylem then matures in the center (Fig. 6-2, E) and the differentiation of the primary xylem is completed (Fig. 6-3, A). In the meantime, the production of secondary xylem continues. By the end of the second year of growth of *Pinus resinosa* roots, the secondary xylem shows the radial seriation of cells typical of cambial products but is still limited to the sides of the primary xylem plate (Fig. 6-3, B). The propagation of cambial activity into the pericycle outside the protoxylem poles occurs after this stage (Wilcox, 1964).

Since the first xylem elements, as well as the first phloem elements, usually differentiate inside of the pericycle (Fig. 6-1), these elements are not in contact with the endodermis. In some grass roots, however, the protoxylem cells may differentiate from the inner products of periclinally divided pericycle cells or from entire pericycle cells. In the latter instance the protoxylem cells touch the endodermis.

The number of protoxylem poles—or of ridges of primary

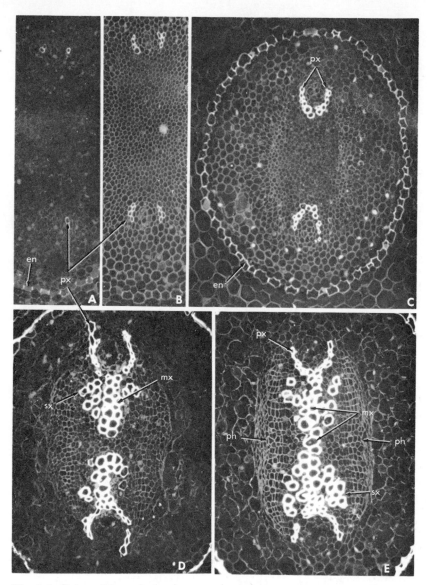

Fig. 6–2. Xylem differentiation in roots of *Pinus resinosa* in transections photographed with ultraviolet light, revealing fluorescence of walls of xylem and endodermis (*en*). The phloem (*ph*) is only weakly revealed in these illustrations. It occurs right and left from the xylem in each figure. (*A, B,* and *C*) Successive stages of centripetal differentiation of protoxylem (*px*). (*D* and *E*) Two stages in centripetal differentiation of metaxylem (*mx*) and beginning of secondary xylem differentiation (*sx*). All × 100. (Courtesy of Hugh Wilcox; *A* and *C* from

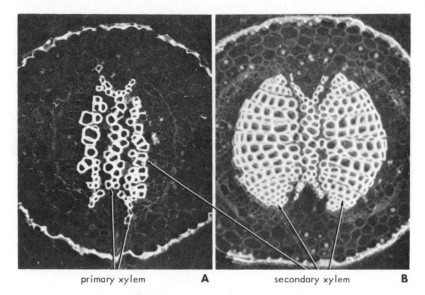

primary xylem   **A**   secondary xylem   **B**

Fig. 6–3. Xylem differentiation in roots of *Pinus resinosa* in transections. Continuation of Fig. 6–2. (*A*) Complete primary xylem flanked by secondary xylem. (*B*) Secondary xylem has increased in amount and shows radial seriation of cells. Both × 100. (Courtesy of Hugh Wilcox.)

xylem—may be highly stable in a given species regardless of the width of the root (e.g., *Pinus resinosa,* Wilcox, 1964). On the other hand, it may be highly variable in the same species. In *Libocedrus decurrens,* for example, the number was found to vary from two to six, and although the larger number was associated with greater widths of the vascular cylinder, the correlation between the number of protoxylem poles and width of vascular cylinder was low (Wilcox, 1962b). The relation between the number of xylem ridges and the size of the root or of the vascular cylinder is generally inconsistent. Torrey (1955) thinks that a more meaningful relation exists between the number of ridges and the size of the procambial cylinder at the level where the xylem pattern is initiated, that is, near the apical meristem; the size differences of procambium are not necessarily correlated with those of the mature vascular cylin-

Fig. 6–2. *(continued).* M. H. Zimmerman (ed.), *The formation of wood in forest trees,* Academic Press, 1964.)

der. The change in the number of ridges may occur during the development of the same root, a matter of considerable importance in the discussions of the role of the apical meristem in determining the vascular pattern in the root. (See next section.)

Differentiation of the phloem in roots has been studied much less completely than that of the xylem, and in seed plants protophloem has been described much more frequently than metaphloem. The circumstance chiefly responsible for this discrepancy is the technical difficulty of obtaining satisfactory microscopic preparations of the root region where metaphloem matures. The protophloem elements in angiosperms differentiate in root parts that are still highly meristematic and may be satisfactorily fixed. Moreover, the protophloem elements stand out sharply among the meristematic cells because of their clear protoplasts (Fig. 6-1, B). The metaphloem elements differentiate in more highly vacuolated regions of the root, which are usually considerably distorted in permanent preparations, and the sieve elements differ little in size, wall thickness, and protoplasmic density from the thin-walled, highly vacuolated parenchyma cells adjoining them. The distinctness of metaphloem is somewhat greater in monocotyledon roots because in this group of plants metaphloem cells are commonly rather wide.

In differentiation of vascular elements from procambium, one must distinguish between maturation of conducting elements and the early cyto-histologic changes that make the various regions of the primary vascular system first discernible. The latitudinal sequence of the early stages of differentiation differs from the sequence in maturation. Commonly the metaxylem shows an earlier cessation of cell division and earlier vacuolation and enlargement of cells than does the more peripheral procambium (Bünning, 1951; Heimsch, 1951). Thus, the early differentiation of the xylem occurs centrifugally, whereas the maturation of the same tissue proceeds centripetally (Fig. 6-2 and 6-3).

The first differentiation of metaxylem, and concomitantly that of the basic pattern of the xylem (diarch, triarch, or other), occurs close to the apical initials. Examples of distances of this differentiation from the apex are 300 μ in *Hordeum* (Heimsch, 1951), 175 μ in *Pisum* (Torrey, 1955), and 100 μ in *Libocedrus* (Wilcox, 1962a). Metaxylem may be recognized before the occurrence of the divisions that give rise to sieve-element mother cells (Torrey, 1955). This feature is easily determined in grass roots, in which the protophloem sieve elements form a characteristic pattern clearly recognizable in transections. It results from two successive oblique anticlinal divisions forming a sieve element and its two companion cells (see Clowes, 1961, pls. 30 and 31, and Hagemann, 1957). A contrasting timing was found in *Abies*, in which the precursory phloem vacuolates earlier than the metaxylem, although the metaxylem precedes the protoxylem in its initial definition (Wilcox, 1954). The early differentiation of metaxylem is one of the characteristics that distinguishes the root from the shoot of the seed plant. In the shoot, procambial divisions cease first in the protoxylem and both differentiation and maturation of the primary xylem thus occur centrifugally.

Longitudinal course of differentiation

The relative simplicity of the root in morphologic aspects is particularly marked if one compares the longitudinal course of differentiation of its vascular system with that of the shoot of a higher plant. The column of procambium is uninterruptedly "left behind" by the growing apical meristem, without leaf traces or leaf gaps. It differentiates continuously and acropetally as a single axial entity. Similarly phloem and xylem tissues differentiate acropetally and continuously.

Figure 6-4 depicts the typical longitudinal sequence of maturation of the first protophloem and protoxylem elements by reference to a dicotyledon root (hop, Miller, 1958). Similar sequence has been observed in roots of a variety of seed plants. Its main features are that the first sieve elements (Fig. 6-1, A and B) mature closer to the apical meristem than do the first xylem elements (Fig. 6-1, C), and both xylem and phloem differentiate acropetally and continuously. Typically also the sieve elements mature in the region of the root which is still rapidly elongating (e.g., Jensen and Kavaljian, 1958; Goodwin and Stepka, 1945) whereas the first xylem commonly matures beyond the region of elongation (e.g., Wilcox, 1964). As a consequence of this relation, the protoxylem of roots may not contain extensible types of secondary wall. Scherer (1904) observed annular and spiral thickenings only in strongly elongating roots.

The distance between the apical meristem and the first mature

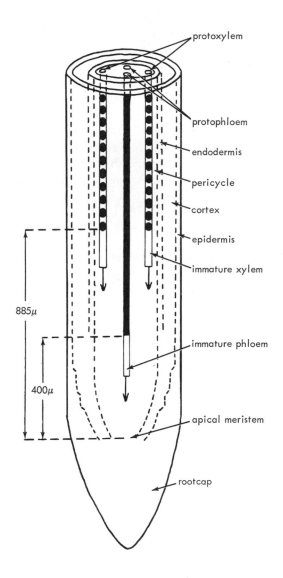

Fig. 6–4. Diagrammatic longitudinal view of root tip of *Humulus lupulus* (hop) with details of initial vascular differentiation. Arrows pointing toward root tip indicate that both xylem and phloem differentiate acropetally. (After Miller [1958].)

phloem and xylem elements varies in relation to the type of root growth. Generally, in rapidly growing roots these distances are greater than in the slowly growing roots. Examples of recorded distances are given in Table 6-1.

Table 6-1
Initial Vascularization in Roots

Genus	Distance in Microns		Reference
	Apex to first phloem element	Apex to first xylem element	
Hordeum	250–750	410–10,000	Heimsch, 1951
Humulus	400	885	Miller, 1958
Nicotiana	260–470	400–2,500	Esau, 1941
Phleum	230	970	Goodwin and Stepka, 1945
Pisum	340	over 5,000	Torrey, 1955

Wilcox (1954) found that in *Abies procera* the phloem matured at 350 μ from the apex in roots growing 6 mm per day and at 150 μ in roots growing 2 mm per day. The protoxylem matured at 7000 μ from the apex in an actively growing root, at 500 μ in a root sampled 4 days after elongation had ceased in preparation for dormancy, and at less than 50 μ in a root long dormant. In *Libocedrus* (Wilcox, 1962a) the distance of mature protoxylem from the apex varied from 400 μ or less in dormant roots to over 5 mm in roots growing more than 5 mm per day.

The metaxylem of active roots matures over a considerable distance and therefore the final maturation of this tissue occurs far from the apex. In *Humulus* (Miller, 1958) this stage was reached 15 mm from the apex; in *Libocedrus*, 13 cm from the apex in a root growing 5 mm per day (Wilcox, 1962a). The slow maturation of the metaxylem explains why tracheary elements with nuclei are so readily found in root tips (Scott, 1963).

The vascularization of lateral roots, which usually arise in the pericycle of the parent root, has not been studied sufficiently to permit generalization regarding the course of differentiation of their vascular connection with the parent root. Thibault (1946) reported that the xylem of the lateral roots of *Daucus* arose independently and then differentiated basipetally to form a connection with the parent root. Torrey (1955), on the other hand, observed that in cultured roots of *Pisum* the xylem of the lateral root, which was derived from pericyclic derivatives, differentiated first and in contact with the protoxylem of the parent root. Subsequently tracheary elements differentiated acropetally in the procambium of the lateral root. Although the vascular system of the main root usually differentiates independently from that of the lateral root, occasionally some vascular tissue differentiation is induced in the parent root during the vascularization of the lateral root (Bünning, 1952a; Fourcroy, 1942).

VASCULARIZATION IN EXPERIMENTALLY TREATED ROOTS

Initially the experimental work on morphogenesis was centered on the apical meristem of the shoot, especially that of the fern (see Wardlaw, 1952), but the root has now received attention. The root is a living system particularly amenable to experimental control of its growth and differentiation (see Torrey, 1963). Experimental work on morphogenesis in roots is frequently designed to discover the mechanism controlling the pattern of vascularization and to explore the role of the apical meristem in this mechanism.

Generally two alternatives are discussed with regard to the seat of the controlling mechanism. One of these states that the pattern in the newly developing root tip is induced acropetally by the existing pattern in the older part of the root. The other proposes that the pattern is under the control of the apical meristem. Methods to study the problem consist of puncturing, incising, or removing and culturing the apices either from normally growing roots or from isolated roots grown in a culture medium. Treatment with growth substances and other chemicals is used alone or in combination with surgical methods.

The early root decapitation studies of Jost (1931-1932) were interpreted as indicating that the older root pattern influenced that in the root part developing after the operation. Jost spoke in particular about the acropetal induction of new vessel members by each row of vessel members present below. Bünning (1952a) tested this view by a modified decapitation technique. He severed a tip about 2 mm long from a *Vicia faba* root (apparently including the rootcap) and applied it to the decapitated and usually further shortened stump of the same root. The two parts united and xylem differentiated in the formerly isolated tip. The differentiation took place even without a union, when a plastic membrane was inserted between the tip and the stump. The vessels in the newly formed root portion were not in line with those below, and the vascular connection between the tip and the stump, when the two were grown together, occurred by bridges of xylem derived from intervening cells. Such results were obtained even if the tip was placed somewhat to the side, over the cortex of the stump.

Bünning (1952a,b) concluded that the vascular pattern was previously determined in the apex but that some inductive effect coming from the existing tissues made possible the realization of this pattern through differentiation. On the basis of anatomic evidence, one would expect the xylem pattern, with the vacuolated and expanded cells of metaxylem toward the center, to be discernible in the first 2 mm of the root; in fact, the protophloem could be in an advanced stage of differentiation or even mature in a root segment that long (Table 6-1). Thus, the discovery of the origin of the pattern required further refinement of techniques.

Efforts in that direction were made by Reinhard and Torrey. Reinhard (1954) divided the root tip of *Pisum* into fragments containing meristematic tissues of different degrees of differentiation; he then studied their ability to regenerate roots in tissue cultures. Explant 1 contained the rootcap and the apical initials; it gave an irregularly proliferating mass of tissue without differentiation. Explant 2 consisted of the apical initials and some subjacent central tissue in which the procambium was delimited by a pericycle; this explant grew irregularly at first but subsequently became differentiated into a cortex and a central zone and under some conditions produced lateral roots. Explants 3 and 4 consisted of two successive portions of procambium below explant 2 (that is, away from the root apex); both gave callous proliferations with some xylary differentiation forming no regular patterns. Explants consisting of parts of young cortex and epidermis differentiated into normal-appearing tissues of the same kind and formed numerous root hairs. Finally, if the cultured root portion contained material corresponding to that included in the first three explants, normal root growth was established without a suture between the original explant and the new growth.

Reinhard (1954) concluded that the older root tissues did not control the activity of the meristematic region. Yet, here again, normal root growth was obtained when a considerable length of the vascular cylinder was present—700 μ to 800 μ below the apical meristem (Reinhard, 1954). At this level the pattern of xylem is determined in *Pisum* root, and according to Torrey (1955), mature protophloem cells are present.

Reinhard's (1954) explant 2 (100 μ to 200 μ below the apical meristem), which Torrey (1963) considers to be at the lower limit of size of root tip that can act autonomously, did not continue normal growth. It sometimes produced lateral roots but formed no terminal apical meristem. Torrey (1955) found in his own experiments that the distal $\frac{1}{2}$ mm of pea root, including some 200 μ below the apex (thus including Reinhard's explant 2 plus rootcap and embryonic cortex), had special nutrient requirements. If these were supplied, the isolated tip grew into a normal root. A tip of this size contained no mature phloem elements (Torrey, 1954, 1955).

Torrey (1955) studied the development of the vascular pattern in the roots derived from isolated $\frac{1}{2}$ mm-long root tips of *Pisum*. Many of the cultured root tips produced the normal triarch pattern, but in some the pattern was reduced to diarch or even monarch. As a root with the reduced pattern elongated, its apical meristem and procambial cylinder became wider and the triarch pattern was restored.

Torrey (1957) also observed the regeneration phenomena in those cultured roots from which the $\frac{1}{2}$ mm of tip was removed and which developed a new apical meristem. In auxin-free medium, the new increment of root developing from a regenerated tip produced either a normal triarch pattern, continuous with the original, or variants of this pattern with more or less pronounced discontinuity in its relation to the pattern in the older root part. With the addition of an inhibitory amount of auxin, the slowly growing roots produced a hexarch pattern. When the root was transferred to a medium containing a lower concentration of auxin, the pattern changed from hexarch to pentarch or tetrarch, and in the control medium, to the characteristic triarch. Under these varying conditions the most consistent result was that an increase in auxin concentration caused an increase in size and number of cells in the latitudinal extent of the procambium near the apex.

In still another experiment, Torrey (1963) allowed roots to regenerate new root tips in a medium to which were added auxin and a rather high concentration of kinetin. Root elongation was reduced and the vascular pattern changed from the usual radially alternate to a concentric one such as is found in secondary growth. After transfer to a control medium, the root reverted to a production of the typical alternate arrangement of xylem and phloem.

Reinhard (1956) observed modifications of the vascular pattern during regeneration of apices after vertical incisions were made in a normally diarch root of *Sinapis*. Two root tips regenerated, one or both of which were sometimes triarch. Usually triarchy changed to diarchy later.

Torrey and Reinhard concluded that the vascular pattern is determined at the apex and by the apex rather than by the more mature region. Torrey (1963) suggests that the distal part of the apical meristem may be regarded as the center of hormone formation. This concept seems to conflict with the well-documented view that the distal part of the apical meristem is low in metabolic activity and in rate of cell division—this region is the quiescent center of Clowes' (1961). According to Torrey (1963), however, the apical meristem might be active in localized production of hormonal substances which at high concentrations are inhibitory to cell division and related metabolic processes. Primary tissue differentiation results in response to a controlled movement of substances in stimulatory concentrations from the apex toward the lower levels where they interact with other factors. Specifically, endogenous hormone levels established by the apex determine the cellular pattern by controlling the frequency and orientation of cell division. Torrey (1951, 1963) finds that formation of vascular cambium is also under hormonal control, but apparently in this instance the hormone is moving acropetally from the basal parts of the root rather than basipetally from the apex.

Morphogenetic research with roots narrows down the problem of pattern control more successfully than does the work with shoots. In the root the hormonal aspects of differentiation are not obscured by the relation between leaf primordia and the apical meristem.

Still, the exact role of the apical meristem in pattern formation in both shoot and root remains to be determined. Torrey (1963) postulates presence of "other factors" with which the hormones supposedly derived from the apex must react before patterned meristematic activity is induced. He also discusses the possibility that differential sensitivity of cells to hormones may be involved in patterned development, but differential sensitivity would in itself indicate patterned behavior.

Vascularization in roots has been considered by Bünning (1951, 1952b) with reference to the concept of inhibitory effects in pattern development. In the differentiating regions, some tissues—the meristemoids—continue meristematic growth and prevent other tissues in the immediate neighborhood from doing the same. Specifically in the root, according to Bünning, the first xylem and phloem meristemoids can occur only at a certain distance from one another, and this interaction produces a pattern. Hagemann (1957) thought that the sequence of development of protophloem in the root of *Hordeum* fits Bünning's concept. Reinhardt (1960), however, reviewing the autonomous change from triarchy to diarchy in experimentally mutilated *Sinapis* roots, suggested that Bünning's hypothesis requires qualification. Before the change from triarchy to diarchy occurs, the disappearing strands of xylem and phloem differentiate progressively closer to their own kind until a complete fusion occurs. Thus, no mutual inhibition appears to exist between two phloem or two xylem meristemoids. Torrey's (1957) experiments, on the other hand, indicate that xylem elements may differentiate within the phloem so that the concept of mutual incompatibility between xylem and phloem may also be questioned.

The relation between rate of root growth and level of maturation of xylem has received some consideration in experimental research. Observing the behavior of excised pea roots treated with metabolic inhibitors, Torrey (1953) concluded that the proximity of mature xylem to the apices of treated roots resulted not only from inhibition of root elongation but also because xylem maturation was accelerated. Phloem differentiation was little affected in the same roots. According to Odhnoff (1963), the differentiation of xylem close to the apices in bean roots treated with gibberellic acid could not be attributed to any inhibiting effect on root growth.

VASCULAR DIFFERENTIATION IN THE EMBRYO

A complete description of primary vascular differentiation of a plant should begin with that in the embryo. Most of the studies on embryos, however, are concerned with the early stages of embryogenesis and those that deal with later stages do not emphasize vascularization.

Procambium

The first delimitation of the vascular region in the embryo parallels that which was described as a delimitation of residual meristem in the shoot (Chapter Three). Enlargement and increased vacuolation of cells in the embryonic cortex and pith block out a tissue region whose cells at first retain the characteristics of the earlier embryonic cells and only gradually assume the procambial form. Usually the first blocking out of the provascular region occurs before the embryo has initiated the growth of the cotyledons (for dicotyledons: Buell, 1952; Miller and Wetmore, 1945a; Nast, 1941; Reeve, 1948b; for monocotyledons: Esau, 1960; for conifers: Spurr, 1949; Sterling, 1949). The authors emphasize that the vascular region is blocked out as a unit and that the phenomenon is continued acropetally in the cotyledons when these develop.

Since the procambium assumes its characteristics gradually, Meyer (1958) interprets the earlier tissue in the vascular region of the apple embryo as a residual meristem, whereas Nast (1941) calls it prodesmogen with reference to the walnut embryo. Spurr (1949) characterizes the provascular meristem in *Pinus* embryo as a procambium in incipient stage. He also states that initially the procambial cells assume an elongated shape not because longitudinal divisions predominate but because transverse divisions are infrequent and the cells elongate. Longitudinal divisions become numerous in the seedling stage. According to Mahlberg (1960), in the embryo of *Nerium oleander* the procambium is delimited first by the establishment of a periclinally dividing zone in the innermost part of the embryonic cortex. In Figure 6-5 these divisions were completed above but were still occurring below (d). The initial provascular region stains more deeply than the adjacent ground

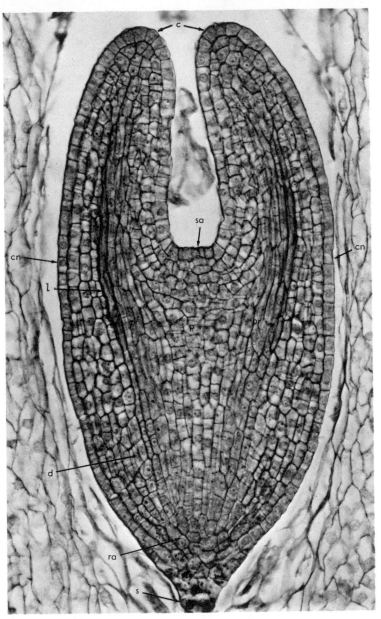

Fig. 6–5. Median longitudinal section of embryo of *Nerium oleander* 400 μ long, from immature seed. Details: *c*, cotyledons; *cn*, cotyledonary node; *d*, result of recent periclinal division in cortex; *l*, laticifer; *p*, pith; *pr*, procambium extending through cotyledons and hypocotyl and converging toward root apex (*ra*); *sa*, shoot apex; *s*, upper part of suspensor. × 340. (From Mahlberg [1960].)

tissue. Just before the cotyledons emerge, longitudinal divisions occur at the future cotyledonary node and progress basipetally toward the suspensor. As is usual in procambium, these divisions are not followed by much expansion of cells and these assume a narrow, elongated shape. Figure 6-5 shows that this procambial characteristic is best expressed at the cotyledonary node (cn) and fades out toward the apices of the cotyledons and toward the suspensor (s). Procambial differentiation in the embryo in Figure 6-5 is far enough advanced to show the inception of laticifer (l) differentiation.

The basipetal progress of procambial differentiation, as demonstrated by the embryo of *Nerium*, agrees with the earlier basipetal progress of vacuolation of the embryonic cortex and pith and with the direction of the general intercalary growth of the hypocotyl. The basipetal progress of differentiation in the hypocotyl is, of course, acropetal with reference to the apical meristem of the root (Fig. 6-5, ra). When later the root develops, its procambium differentiates in continuity with that of the hypocotyl.

The foregoing discussion indicates that the phenomena of early vascularization in embryos are similar to those observed in the shoot. Differentiation of the ground tissue blocks out a meristem precursory to procambium and associated parenchyma of the vascular region. Before the blocking out is completed, procambial differentiation is initiated. In the shoot of the seed plant this procambium is that of the leaf traces (Chapter Three). In the embryo also the relation of the procambium to the cotyledons is perceptible (Fig. 6-5). The procambium in the hypocotyl, at least in its upper part, is associated with the cotyledons as leaf traces are with leaves.

Proper understanding of the embryonic development of the vascular interrelation between the cotyledons, the hypocotyl, and the root is fundamental for the interpretation of the shoot and root connection (transition region) and of the origin of the plant as a coordinated shoot-root system. If the apical meristems determine the patterns of vascularization in the subjacent axes, embryonic development establishes two centers of determination, each inducing its distinct pattern. The transition region would then be the part of the plant in which the influence of the two centers is correlated or reconciled.

Embryos vary in degree of differentiation of their organs in mature seeds. Some consist of cotyledons and a hypocotyl-root axis, others may have one or more leaves on the epicotyl produced by its apical meristem. A radicle instead of only a root meristem may be present. The radicle shows a disposition of the procambium similar to that in the future root, whereas the epicotyl has shoot structure. The procambium of the cotyledons, the hypocotyl, and the radicle is one continuous tissue system. The connection of the epicotyl with this system is an aspect that still remains to be fully investigated. Does the epicotyl behave like an adventitious bud and develop its procambial connection with the hypocotyl by basipetally differentiating strands, or is the connection formed by an acropetal blocking out of a vascular meristem continuous from hypocotyl to epicotyl apex at all times? Conceivably, the pattern of differentiation of this connection varies in relation to the timing of the epicotyl development.

In dicotyledons the two first leaves on the epicotyl usually are in a decussate arrangement with the cotyledons. Thus, sections made perpendicular to those of the median plane through the cotyledons are necessary for showing the longitudinal extent of the first traces to the epicotyl; and complementary serial transections are essential just as they are in the study of vascularization in adult shoots.

According to Pellegrini's (1956) study on the epicotyls of *Cassia*, *Koelreuteria*, and *Cardiospermum*, the two sites on the apical meristem where the first two leaf primordia are to develop are connected to the procambium of the hypocotyl by a tissue precursory to the procambium. Miller and Wetmore (1945a,b) and Reeve (1948a,b) reported an initial continuity of procambium between the epicotyl and the hypocotyl in certain other dicotyledons. Camefort (1950), on the other hand, stated that the traces of the first pair of leaves on the epicotyl of *Cupressus* differentiated basipetally. According to Taylor (1957), in the monocotyledon embryo of *Zostera marina*, which produces three leaf primordia on the epicotyl, the midvein procambium of each primordium differentiates acropetally from the hypocotyl, whereas the lateral procambial strands of two older primordia are initiated at the base of the primordia and then follow a bidirectional course.

Maturation of the first vascular elements

Differentiation of the first vascular elements in embryos is another topic on which information is scanty, particularly with regard to the phloem. In the embryo of *Pinus strobus* Spurr (1950) was able to distinguish between the phloic and the xylary parts of procambium, a feature frequently present in adult shoots (Esau, 1953a). The phloic procambium differs from the xylary in having narrower, more densely stained cells and less orderly cell arrangement. Miller and Wetmore (1945a) described phloic and xylary procambium in *Phlox* and emphasized the continuity of both throughout the embryo.

Maturation of the first vascular elements in the embryo or later, in the seedling, follows a course which does not necessarily coincide with that of the procambium. At least xylem differentiation is usually discontinuous. According to Miller and Wetmore (1945a), for example, in the *Phlox* embryo some mature xylem elements occur in several loci in the cotyledon. Moens (1963) observed scattered tracheary elements in the hypocotyl of occasional mature embryos of *Coffea*. It is frequently uncertain whether the xylem elements referred to by the authors are mature, that is, free of living protoplasts, or whether they have secondary walls but are still living cells.

Mature or differentiating phloem elements have been reported in some embryos (see Esau, 1943c). Mature phloem was rarely found in the *Phlox* embryo although, as mentioned, mature xylem was present (Miller and Wetmore, 1945a). Nast (1941) recorded some xylem and phloem in the embryo of *Juglans*. The first sieve tubes appeared at the lower levels of the hypocotyl, the first xylem in relation to the cotyledonary traces. Millington and Fisk (1956) found no mature vascular elements in the embryo of *Xanthium*.

VASCULAR DIFFERENTIATION IN THE SEEDLING

Vascularization of the seedling is of particular theoretical interest in that it represents the first mature realization of the vascular coordination between shoot and root foreshadowed in the procambial system of the embryo. The sequence of differentiation of this coordination might conceivably reflect the distinct influences of apical meristems at the two poles of the embryo. At the shoot pole the vascular system differentiates under the influence of leaves, at the root pole as a purely axial structure. Exploration of these morphogenetic aspects in the seedling is still to be made. The extensive literature on the transition region deals with the vascular connection between the shoot and the root at some early stage of development, but the literature is incomplete with regard to the development of this connection.

The basic aspects of the transition region are best illustrated by reference to a relatively simple type found in dicotyledons (Fig. 6-6). Transition, that is, change from a typical root structure to the typical shoot structure, or the converse, occurs within the system connecting the cotyledon or cotyledons with the root (e.g., Weaver, 1960, and Fig. 6-6). Within the leaf traces of the cotyledons, the xylem is reoriented from the exarch condition typical of the root (Fig. 6-6, G) to the endarch one (Fig. 6-6, A, H, and I); and the arrangement of xylem and phloem is changed from alternate (Fig. 6-6, F and G) to collateral (Fig. 6-6, I). If pith is absent in the root (Fig. 6-6, G), it appears in the transition region (Fig. 6-6, B–F). Variations in structure of the transition region depend on the number of leaf traces to the cotyledons and the exact levels at which the fundamental changes occur. The leaf traces of the epicotyl may differentiate to variable distances in the hypocotyl and complicate the pattern in the transition region (Fig. 6-6, A–D).

A more complex transition region is illustrated in Figures 6-7 to 6-9 based on Arnott's (1962) study of *Yucca*. Figure 6-7, A, shows the structure of the cotyledonary node of *Yucca whipplei*. The first leaf of the epicotyl has three major traces, the cotyledon has two. The five traces are shown connected into a column below the cotyledonary node. In the seedling this column is prolonged below into the root. The histological details of the root-shoot transition in the same species of *Yucca* appear in Figures 6-8 and 6-9. In Figure 6-8, A, leaf 1, which is enclosed in the cotyledonary sheath, has one procambial strand. The two cotyledonary bundles are collateral and their xylem is endarch. At a lower level (Fig. 6-8, B) the first leaf has three procambial strands (compare with Figure 6-7, A). The cotyledonary bundles appear successively closer to the first leaf, and the bundles of the cotyledon and the first leaf form a single group, cut on bias, in Figure 6-9, A. The clear file of cells in this group is a sieve tube cut lengthwise because of its horizontal orientation

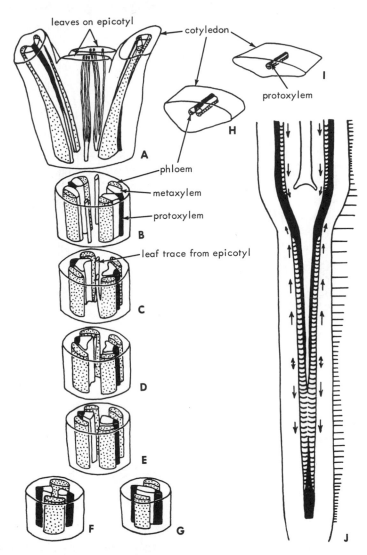

Fig. 6–6. Vasculature of a Chenopodiaceae seedling. (*A–G*) Successive levels showing vascular connection between cotyledons and root (transition). (*H* and *I*) Sections of a cotyledon. Details: black, protoxylem; white, metaxylem; stippled, phloem. Exarch xylem in *C–G*; endarch xylem in upper part of *A*, and in *H* and *I*; transitional condition in *B* and lower part of *A*. (*J*) Diagram of seedling showing direction (arrows) of xylem (horizontal hatching) differentiation. Black, procambium. Scale to the right indicates comparative elongation of different parts of seedling. (Adapted from Bisalputra [1961].)

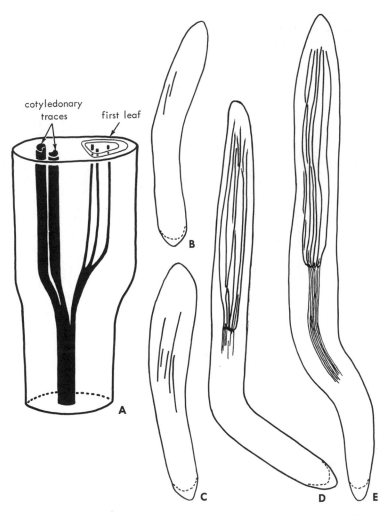

Fig. 6–7. Vasculature of *Yucca* seedling. (*A*) Cotyledonary node of *Y. whipplei.* Two traces to cotyledon, three to first leaf. (*B–E*) Differentiation of xylem in seedling of *Y. brevifolia.* (After Arnott [1962].)

(Fig. 6-7, A, level at top of the column). The relative position of xylem and phloem is changed below this level. In Figure 6-9, B, the phloem occurs in five strands. The xylem is somewhat irregularly arranged. The root level (Fig. 6-9, C) shows vascular tissues in

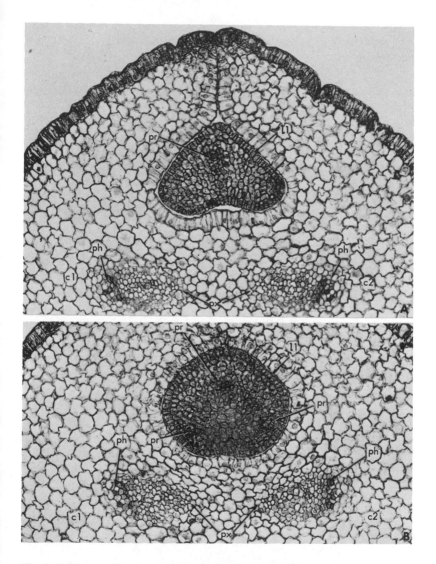

Fig. 6–8. Transections of two levels of *Yucca whipplei* seedling. (*A*) higher level. First leaf (*ll*), with one procambial strand (*pr*), enclosed in cotyledonary sheath with two collateral bundles, *c1* and *c2*. (*B*) Lower level. First leaf has three procambial strands (arrows). Details: *c*, cotyledonary bundle; *ll*, first leaf above cotyledon; *ph*, phloem; *pr*, procambium; *px*, protoxylem. Both × 146. (From Arnott [1962].)

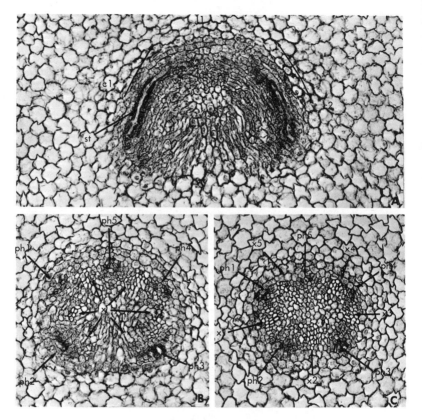

Fig. 6–9. Transections of *Yucca whipplei* seedling at three levels below those shown in Fig. 6–8. (*A*) Cotyledonary traces (*c*1 and *c*2) are cut on bias; they are indistinguishable from the supply to first leaf (*l*1) with which they appear to be merged. (*B*) Five phloem strands (*ph*1-*ph*5); the xylem (*x*) is partly reoriented from collateral to alternate position with regard to phloem. (*C*) Root structure; alternate arrangement of xylem and phloem. Details: *c*, cotyledonary traces; *l*1, leaf trace of first leaf; *ph*, phloem; *st*, sieve tube; *x*, xylem. All × 146. (From Arnott [1962].)

alternate radial arrangement, with the xylem exarch. The endarchy (Fig. 6-8, A) and exarchy (Fig. 6-9, C) are revealed by the position of the xylem poles in relation to the subsequent xylem. The xylem was not mature in this seedling. Later the center of the root is occupied by metaxylem.

The figures just discussed indicate that in *Yucca* not only the cotyledon but also the first leaf has a direct vascular connection with the root. Possibly phloem pole 5 (Fig. 6-9, C) was part of the vascular supply of this leaf. According to Ginieis (1950), in another monocotyledon, the palm *Chamaerops*, the first leaf is directly connected with the root.

Xylem differentiation has been partially studied in a number of species. Several stages of this differentiation are shown in Figure 6-7, B–E, for *Yucca brevifolia*. The xylem is initiated in the cotyledon (Fig. 6-7, B), then differentiates acropetally in the cotyledon and basipetally toward the cotyledonary node (Fig. 6-7, D), and finally appears in the axis below the cotyledonary node (Fig. 6-7, E). In a more advanced stage in the seedling of *Yucca brevifolia*, the xylem of the first leaf is seen connected with that of the cotyledon below the cotyledonary node (Fig. 6-10).

The early xylem differentiation in *Yucca* is mostly continuous. In *Coffea canefora* this tissue matures initially in separate loci in the cotyledons and in the root (Moens, 1963). The xylem differentiating basipetally from the cotyledons joins the xylem differentiating from the root poles toward the hypocotyl, that is, basipetally with respect to the root. Lehmberg (1923-1924) recorded rather similar xylem differentiation in *Helianthus* seedling, Bisalputra (1961) in certain Chenopodiaceae (Fig. 6-6, J), and Marsden and Bailey (1955) in *Clerodendron*. The first mature xylem was found at the bases of the cotyledons and in the root. A bidirectional course of maturation occurred from all three loci, and the union occurred in the hypocotyl. Goodwin (1942) found two loci of initial differentiation of xylem in the seedling of a grass, *Avena*. The first locus was at the scutellar node, from which the xylem differentiated upward through the internode. The second was at the coleoptilar node, with the subsequent xylem differentiating downward through the internode.

The course of phloem differentiation in seedlings is practically unknown. The reason for this deficiency is the relative inconspicuousness of the sieve elements of the primary phloem and the frequently poor preservation of phloem. The use of specialized techniques such as polarization (e.g., Bisalputra and Esau, 1964) or fluorescence microscopy (e.g., Wetmore and Rier, 1963) should facilitate phloem studies in embryos and seedlings.

Miller and Wetmore (1945b) obtained some data on phloem

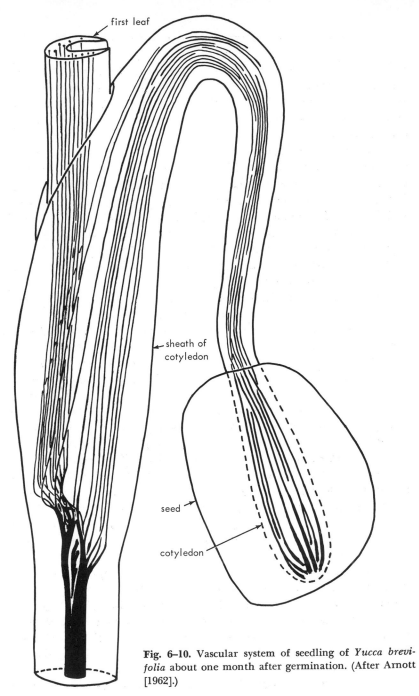

first leaf

sheath of
cotyledon

seed

cotyledon

Fig. 6–10. Vascular system of seedling of *Yucca brevi-folia* about one month after germination. (After Arnott [1962].)

differentiation in seedlings of *Phlox*. The tissue matured first at the base (toward the root) of the hypocotyl, then upward and downward. In contrast, the xylem became mature first at the base of the cotyledons. Further differentiation occurred bidirectionally. Some xylem matured before the phloem, in the embryo, but when phloem differentiation began it progressed more rapidly than that of the xylem.

The vascular organization of the seedling plays a primary role in discussions of the morphologic significance of the transition region (see Duchaigne, 1951). The principal controversy centers on the question of whether the vascular system is a unit composed of equivalent parts or consists of two systems connected developmentally with one another (see Esau, 1953b). The discussions are usually based on the patterns of xylem differentiation. As far as it was investigated, the xylem may indeed show a discontinuous initial maturation which could be interpreted as indicating the presence of two systems. But the initial delimitation of the procambium reveals a primary unity of the system. If one adopts the concept of the double nature of the vascular system on the basis of xylem differentiation alone, then the shoot of the higher plant should also be interpreted as a composite of units (phytons) built around the leaf-trace xylem. In view of the abundant evidence for a strong dependence of the pattern of xylem differentiation on distribution of hormonal substances, the morphologic significance of the discontinuous xylem initiation may be questioned.

CONCLUSION

The vascular differentiation of roots involves fewer problems of interpretation than does that of the shoot. A continuous acropetal differentiation of procambium, phloem, and xylem with no relation to lateral organs is characteristic of the root. The relative simplicity of root organization makes this organ especially suitable for morphogenetic investigations. Experimental studies have provided strong evidence in support of the concept that hormonal substances are important agents in the control of vascular patterns, and the studies suggest that the apical meristem may be the source of these substances. Consequently, the control of differentiation by the apical meristem has been discussed largely in terms of hormonal relations. The embryonic vascular system of the sporophyte has been interpreted as a unit with regard to its initial ontogenetic de-limitation. The recognition of this unity must be correlated with the concept that the organization of the young sporophyte occurs under two opposing influences emanating from the two poles, the shoot meristem and the root meristem. The discontinuous xylem differentiation has been used to interpret the seedling structure as a composite of two systems; but the discontinuities may be related to the patterned distribution of auxins in an initially unified procambial system.

Bibliography

ALLSOPP, A., 1964. "Shoot morphogenesis," *Ann. Rev. Plant Physiol.*, 15: 225–254.

ANDREWS, H. N., 1961. *Studies in paleobotany*, New York: John Wiley and Sons.

ARNOTT, H. J., 1962. "The seed, germination, and seedling of *Yucca*," *Univ. Calif., Publ., Bot.*, 35: 1–164.

BAILEY, I. W., 1953. "Evolution of tracheary tissue of land plants," *Amer. J. Bot.*, 40: 4–8.

BAIN, H. F., 1940. "Origin of adventitious shoots in decapitated cranberry seedlings," *Bot. Gaz.*, 101: 872–880.

BALFOUR, ENA, 1957. "The development of vascular systems in *Macropiper excelsum* Forst. I. The embryo and the seedling," *Phytomorph.*, 7: 354–364.

———, 1958. "The development of the vascular systems of *Macropiper excelsum* Forst. II. The mature stem," *Phytomorph.*, 8: 224–233.

BALL, ERNEST, 1949. "The shoot apex and normal plant of *Lupinus albus* L., bases for experimental morphology," *Amer. J. Bot.*, 36: 440–454.

———, 1950. "Differentiation in a callus culture of *Sequoia sempervirens*," *Growth*, 14: 295–325.

———, 1952a. "Morphogenesis of shoots after isolation of the shoot apex of *Lupinus albus*," *Amer. J. Bot.*, 39: 167–191.

———, 1952b. "Experimental division of the shoot apex of *Lupinus albus* L.," *Growth*, 16: 151–174.

BARTELS, FRITZ, 1960. "Zur Entwicklung der Keimpflanze von *Epilobium hirsutum*. II. Die im Vegetationspunkt während eines Plastochrons ablaufenden Zellteilungen," *Flora*, 149: 206–224.

BARTHELMESS, ALFRED, 1935. "Ueber den Zusammenhang zwischen Blattstellung und Stelenbau unter besonderer Berücksichtigung der Koniferen," *Bot. Arch.*, 37: 207–260.

BECK, C. B., 1957. "*Tetraxylopteris schmidtii gen. et sp. nov.*, a probable pteridosperm precursor from the Devonian of New York," *Amer. J. Bot.*, 44: 350–367.

BERSILLON, GASTON, 1955. "Recherches sur les Papavéracées. Contribution à l'étude du développement des Dicotylédones herbacées," *Ann. des Sci. Nat., Bot.*, sér. 11, 16: 225–447.

BIERHORST, D. W., 1960. "Observations on tracheary elements," *Phytomorph.*, 10: 249–305.

138 · BIBLIOGRAPHY

BISALPUTRA, THANA, 1961. "Anatomical and morphological studies in the Chenopodiaceae. II. Vascularization of the seedling," *Austral. J. Bot.*, 9: 1–19.

———, and ESAU, K., 1964. "Polarized light study of phloem differentiation in embryo of *Chenopodium album*," *Bot. Gaz.*, 125: 1–7.

BLYTH, AMÉLIE, 1958. "Origin of primary extraxylary fibers in dicotyledons," *Calif. Univ., Publ., Bot.*, 30: 145–232.

BOKE, N. H., 1949. "Development of the stamens and carpels in *Vinca rosea* L.," *Amer. J. Bot.*, 36: 535–547.

BOODLE, L. A., 1903. "Comparative anatomy of the Hymenophyllaceae, Schizaeaceae and Gleicheniaceae. IV. Further observations on *Schizaea*," *Ann. Bot.*, 17: 511–537.

BOWER, F. O., 1921. "Size, a neglected factor in stelar morphology," *Roy. Soc. Edinburgh Proc.*, 41: 1–25.

———, 1923. *The ferns.* Vol. 1. *Analytical examination of the criteria of comparison*, Cambridge: University Press.

———, 1926. *The ferns.* Vol. II. *The eusporangiate and other relatively primitive ferns*, Cambridge: University Press.

BREBNER, GEORGE, 1902. "On the anatomy of *Danaea* and other Marattiaceae," *Ann. Bot.*, 16: 517–552.

BROWN, C. L., 1964. "The influence of external pressure on the differentiation of cells and tissues cultured in vitro," pp. 389–404 in M. H. Zimmermann (ed.), *The formation of wood in forest trees*, New York: Academic Press.

———, and SAX, K., 1962. "The influence of pressure on the differentiation of secondary tissues," *Amer. J. Bot.*, 49: 683–691.

BUCHHOLZ, MARIA, 1920. "Über die Wasserleitungsbahnen in den interkalaren Wachstumszonen monokotyler Sprosse," *Flora*, 14: 119–186.

BUELL, K. M., 1952. Developmental morphology in *Dianthus*. I. Structure of the pistil and seed development," *Amer. J. Bot.*, 39: 194–210.

BÜNNING, ERWIN, 1951. "Über die Differenzierungsvorgänge in der Cruciferenwurzel," *Planta*, 39: 126–153.

———, 1952a. "Weitere Untersuchungen über die Differenzierungsvorgänge in Wurzeln," *Ztschr. f. Bot.*, 40: 385–406.

———, 1952b. "Morphogenesis in plants," *Surv. Biol. Progr.*, 2: 105–140.

BUVAT, ROGER, 1955. "Sur la structure et le fonctionnement du point végétatif de *Selaginella caulescens* Spring., var. *amoena*," *Acad. des Sci. Compt. Rend.*, 241: 1833–1836.

CAMEFORT, HENRI, 1950. "Anomalies foliaires et variations phyllotaxiques chez les plantules de *Cupressus sempervirens*," *Rev. Gén. Bot.*, 57: 348–371.

———, 1956. "Étude de la structure du point végétatif et des variations phyllotaxiques chez quelques Gymnospermes," *Ann. Sci. Nat., Bot.*, Sér. 11, 17: 1–185.

CAMPBELL, D. H., 1921. "The eusporangiate ferns and the stelar theory," *Amer. J. Bot.*, 8: 303–314.

CAMUS, GUY, 1949. "Recherches sur le rôle des bourgeons dans les phénomènes de morphogénèse," *Rev. Cytol., Paris*, 11: 1–199.

CARLQUIST, SHERWIN, 1961. *Comparative plant anatomy*, New York: Holt, Rinehart and Winston.

CHAMPAGNAT, MARGUERITE, 1955. "Origine épidermique des bourgeons axillaires sur l'épicotyle de *Linaria chalepensis* Mill.," *Acad. des Sci. Compt. Rend.*, **240**: 1264–1266.

CHEADLE, V. I., 1953. "Independent origin of vessels in the monocotyledons and dicotyledons," *Phytomorph.*, **3**: 23–44.

CHURCH, A. H., 1904. "The principles of phyllotaxis," *Ann. Bot.*, **18**: 227–243.

CLOWES, F. A. L., 1961. *Apical meristems*, Botanical Monographs Vol. 2. Oxford: Blackwell Scientific Publications.

CLUTTER, M. E., 1960. "Hormonal induction of vascular tissue in tobacco pith in vitro," *Science*, **132**: 548–549.

CUÉNOD, A., 1951. "Du rôle de la feuille dans l'edification de la tige," *Soc. Sci. Nat. Tunisie Bul.*, **4**: 3–15.

CUTTER, E. G., 1959. "On a theory of phyllotaxis and histogenesis," *Biol. Rev., Cambridge Phil. Soc.*, **34**: 243–263.

DAVIS, E. L., 1961. "Medullary bundles in the genus *Dahlia* and their possible origin," *Amer. J. Bot.*, **48**: 108–113.

DE MAGGIO, A. E., WETMORE, R. H., and MOREL, G., 1963. "Induction de tissu vasculaire dans le prothalle de Fougère," *Acad. des Sci. Compt. Rend.*, **256**: 5196–5199.

DENNE, M. P., 1960. "Leaf development of *Narcissus pseudonarcissus* L. II. The comparative development of scale and foliage leaf," *Ann. Bot.*, **24**: 32–47.

DE SLOOVER, JACQUES, 1958. "Recherches sur l'histogénèse des tissus conducteurs. II. Le sens longitudinal de la différenciation du procambium, du xylème et du phloème chez *Coleus, Ligustrum, Anagallis* et *Taxus*," *Cellule*, **59**: 55–202.

DORMER, K. J., 1945. "An investigation of the taxonomic value of shoot structure in angiosperms with special reference to Leguminosae," *Ann. Bot.*, **9**: 141–153.

———, 1954. "The acacian type of vascular system and some of its derivatives. I. Introduction, Menispermaceae, Lardizabalaceae, Berberidaceae," *New Phytol.*, **53**: 301–311.

———, 1955a. "*Azarum europaeum*—a critical case in vascular morphology," *New Phytol.*, **54**: 338–342.

———, 1955b. "Mathematical aspects of plant development," *Discovery*, **16**: 59–64.

DUCHAIGNE, A. L., 1951. *Le passage de la racine à la tige*, Thesis, Poitiers Univ., 134 p., Poitiers: Société Française D'Imprimerie.

ERICKSON, R. O., 1959. "Patterns of cell growth and differentiation in plants," Chap. 12, pp. 497–535 in J. Brachet and A. E. Mirsky (eds.), *The Cell. Biochemistry, Physiology, Morphology*, Vol. 1, New York: Academic Press.

ESAU, KATHERINE, 1938. "Ontogeny and structure of the phloem of tobacco," *Hilgardia*, **11**: 343–424.

———, 1941. "Phloem anatomy of tobacco affected with curly top and mosaic," *Hilgardia*, **13**: 437–490.

———, 1942. "Vascular differentiation in the vegetative shoot of *Linum*. I. The procambium," *Amer. J. Bot.*, **29**: 738–747.

———, 1943a. "Vascular differentiation in the vegetative shoot of *Linum*. II. The first phloem and xylem," *Amer. J. Bot.*, **30**: 248–255.

———, 1943b. "Vascular differentiation in the vegetative shoot of *Linum*. III. The origin of the bast fibers," *Amer. J. Bot.*, **30**: 579–586.

———, 1943c. "Origin and development of primary vascular tissues in seed plants," *Bot. Rev.*, **9**: 125–206.

———, 1945. "Vascularization of the vegetative shoots of *Helianthus* and *Sambucus*," *Amer. J. Bot.*, **32**: 18–29.

———, 1950. "Development and structure of the phloem tissue. II.," *Bot. Rev.*, **16**: 67–114.

———, 1953a. "Anatomical differentiation in shoot and root axes," Chap. 5, pp. 69–100 in W. E. Loomis (ed.), *Growth and differentiation in plants*, Ames, Iowa: Iowa State College Press.

———, 1953b. *Plant anatomy*, New York: John Wiley and Sons.

———, 1954. "Primary vascular differentiation in plants," *Biol. Rev., Cambridge Phil. Soc.*, **29**: 46–86.

———, 1960. *Anatomy of seed plants*, New York: John Wiley and Sons.

———, 1961. *Plants, viruses, and insects*, Cambridge, Massachusetts: Harvard University Press.

———, CHEADLE, V. I., and GIFFORD, E. M., JR., 1953. "Comparative structure and possible trends of specialization of the phloem," *Amer. J. Bot.*, **40**: 9–19.

EZELARAB, G. E., and DORMER, K. J., 1963. "The organization of the primary vascular system in Ranunculaceae," *Ann. Bot.*, **27**: 23–38.

FLASKÄMPER, P., 1910. "Untersuchungen über die Abhängigkeit der Gefäss- und Sklerenchymbildung von äusseren Faktoren nebst einigen Bemerkungen über die angebliche Heterorhizie bei Dicotylen," *Flora*, **101**: 181–219.

FOSKET, D. E., and ROBERTS, L. W., 1964. "Induction of wound-vessel differentiation in isolated *Coleus* stem segments in vitro," *Amer. J. Bot.*, **51**: 19–25.

FOSTER, A. S., 1952. "Foliar venation in angiosperms from an ontogenetic standpoint," *Amer. J. Bot.*, **39**: 752–766.

———, and GIFFORD, E. M., JR., 1959. *Comparative morphology of vascular plants*, San Francisco: W. H. Freeman and Co.

FOURCROY, MADELEINE, 1942. "Perturbations anatomiques intéressant le faisceau vasculaire de la racine au voisinage des radicelles," *Ann. des Sci. Nat., Bot.*, Sér. 11, **3**: 177–198.

FUKUMOTO, K., 1960. "Studies on adventitious bud formation. I. Morphological and histological observations on the adventitious buds on tomato leaves," *Bot. Mag. Tokyo*, **73**: 348–354.

GALINAT, W. C., 1959. "The phytomer in relation to floral homologies in the American Maydeae," *Bot. Mus. Leaflets, Harvard Univ.*, 19: 1–32.

GARRISON, RHODA, 1949a. "Origin and development of axillary buds: *Syringa vulgaris* L.," *Amer. J. Bot.*, 36: 205–213.

———, 1949b. "Origin and development of axillary buds: *Betula papyrifera* March. and *Euptelea polyandra* Sieb. et Zucc.," *Amer. J. Bot.*, 36: 379–389.

GAUTHERET, R. J., 1959. *La culture des tissus végétaux. Techniques et réalisations*, Paris: Masson et Cie.

GIFFORD, E. M., JR., 1951. "Ontogeny of the vegetative axillary bud in *Drimys Winteri* var. *chilensis*," *Amer. J. Bot.*, 38: 234–243.

———, 1954. "The shoot apex in angiosperms," *Bot. Rev.*, 20: 477–529.

———, and TEPPER, H. B., 1961. "Ontogeny of the inflorescence in *Chenopodium album*," *Amer. J. Bot.*, 48: 657–667.

———, — ———, 1962. "Ontogenetic and histochemical changes in the vegetative shoot tip of *Chenopodium album*," *Amer. J. Bot.*, 49: 902–911.

GINIEIS, C., 1950. "Contribution à l'étude anatomique des plantules de palmiers (1): la plantule de *Chamaerops humilis* L.," *Paris Mus. Natl. d'Hist. Nat. Bul.*, 22: 510–517.

GIROLAMI, GUIDO, 1953. "Relation between phyllotaxis and primary vascular organization in *Linum*," *Amer. J. Bot.*, 40: 618–625.

———, 1954. "Leaf histogenesis in *Linum usitatissimum*," *Amer. J. Bot.*, 41: 264–273.

GOLUB, S. J., and WETMORE, R. H., 1948. "Studies of development in the vegetative shoot of *Equisetum arvense* L. II. The mature shoot," *Amer. J. Bot.*, 35: 767–781.

GOODWIN, R. H., 1942. "On the development of xylary elements in the first internode of *Avena* in dark and light," *Amer. J. Bot.*, 29: 818–828.

———, and STEPKA, W., 1945. "Growth and differentiation in the root tip of *Phleum pratense*," *Amer. J. Bot.*, 32: 36–46.

GULLINE, H. F., 1960. "Experimental morphogenesis in adventitious buds in flax," *Austral. J. Bot.*, 8: 1–10.

GUNCKEL, J. E., and WETMORE, R. H., 1946a. "Studies of development in long shoots and short shoots of *Ginkgo biloba* L. I. The origin and pattern of development in the cortex, pith and procambium," *Amer. J. Bot.*, 33: 285–295.

———, — ———, 1946b. "Studies of development in long shoots and short shoots of *Ginkgo biloba* L. II. Phyllotaxis and the organization of the primary vascular system; primary phloem and primary xylem," *Amer. J. Bot.*, 33: 532–543.

GUSTIN, R., and DE SLOOVER, J., 1955. "Recherches sur l'histogénèse des tissus conducteurs. Problèmes posés et données acquises," *Cellule*, 57: 97–128.

GUTTENBERG, H. VON, 1960. "Grundzüge der Histogenese höherer Pflanzen. I. Die Angiospermen," *Handbuch der Pflanzenanatomie*, Vol. 8, Part 3.

HAGEMANN, RUDOLF, 1957. "Anatomische Untersuchungen an Gerstenwurzeln," *Kulturpflanze*, 5: 75–107.

HAGEMANN, WOLFGANG, 1963. "Weitere Untersuchungen zur Organisation des Sprossscheitelmeristems; der Vegetationspunkt traubiger Floreszenzen," *Bot. Jahrb.*, **82**: 273–315.

———, 1964. "Vergleichende Untersuchungen zur Entwicklungsgeschichte des Farnsprosses I. Morphogenese und Histogenese am Sprossscheitel leptosporangiater Farne," *Beitr. Biol. Pflanzen*, **40**: 27–64.

HANSTEIN, JOHANNES, 1858. "Über den Zusammenhang der Blattstellung mit dem Bau des dicotylen Holzringes," *Jahrb. Wiss. Bot.*, **1**: 233–283.

HARA, NOBURU, 1958. "Structure of the vegetative shoot apex and development of the leaf in the Ericaceae and their allies," *Fac. Sci. J. Univ. Tokyo*, Sec. III, *Bot.*, **7**: 367–450.

HEGEDÜS, ÁBEL, 1954. "Die Differenzierung der Meristeme im Sprossvegetationskegel," *Acta Bot. Acad. Sien. Hungar.* (Budapest), **1**: 47–59.

HEIMSCH, CHARLES, 1951. "Development of vascular tissues in barley roots," *Amer. J. Bot.*, **38**: 523–537.

———, 1960. "A new aspect of cortical development in roots," *Amer. J. Bot.*, **47**: 195–201.

HELM, JOHANNES, 1931. "Untersuchungen über die Differenzierung der Sprossscheitelmeristeme von Dikotylen unter besonderer Berücksichtigung des Prokambiums," *Planta*, **15**: 105–191.

———, 1932. "Über die Beeinflussung der Sprossgewebe-Differenzierung durch Entfernen junger Blattanlagen," *Planta*, **16**: 607–621.

HUBER, BRUNO, 1956. "Die Gefässleitung," *Handb. der Pflanzenphysiol.*, **3**: 541–582.

INOUYE, RIUKITI, 1956. "Anatomical studies on the vascular system of *Mirabilis Jalapa* L.," *Bot. Mag. Tokyo*, **69**: 554–559.

IOSSA, M., 1914. "Le développement de l'appareil conducteur dans les rhizomes des Osmundacées et Gleichéniacées," Thesis, *Trav. Inst. Bot. Univ. Genève*, Sér. 8, Fasc. 12, 42 p.

JACOBS, W. P., 1947. "The development of gynophore of the peanut plant, *Arachis hypogaea* L. I. The distribution of mitoses, the region of greatest elongation, and the maintenance of vascular continuity in the intercalary meristem," *Amer. J. Bot.*, **34**: 361–370.

———, 1952. "The role of auxin in differentiation of xylem around a wound," *Amer. J. Bot.*, **39**: 301–309.

———, 1954. "Acropetal auxin transport and xylem regeneration—a quantitative study," *Amer. Naturalist*, **88**: 327–337.

———, and MORROW, I. B. 1957. "A quantitative study of xylem development in the vegetative shoot apex of *Coleus*," *Amer. J. Bot.*, **44**: 823–842.

———, — ———, 1958. "Quantitative relations between stages of leaf development and differentiation of sieve tubes," *Science*, **128**: 1084–1085.

———, and RAGHAVAN, V., 1962. "Studies in the histogenesis and physiology of *Perilla*. I. Quantitative analysis of flowering in *P. frutescens* (L.) Britt.," *Phytomorph.*, **12**: 144–167.

JENSEN, W. A., and KAVALJIAN, L. G., 1958. "An analysis of cell morphology and the periodicity of division in root tip of *Allium cepa*," *Amer. J. Bot.*, 45: 365–372.

JOST, LUDWIG, 1931–1932. "Die Determinierung der Wurzelstruktur," *Ztschr. f. Bot.*, 25: 481–522.

KAAN-ALBEST, ANITA VON, 1934. "Anatomische und physiologische Untersuchungen über die Entstehung von Siebröhrenverbindungen," *Ztschr. f. Bot.*, 27: 1–94.

KALBE, LOTHAR, 1962. "Histogenetische Untersuchungen an Sprossvegetationspunkten dikotyler Holzpflanzen," *Flora*, 152: 279–314.

KAPLAN, REINHARD, 1936. "Die Differenzierung des Sprossscheitelmeristems bei einigen Piperaceen, kleinblättrigen Dikotylen, Monokotylen und Gymnospermen," *Planta*, 25: 302–306.

———, 1937. "Ueber die Bildung der Stele aus dem Urmeristem von Pteridophyten und Spermatophyten," *Planta*, 27: 224–268.

KERNS, K. R., COLLINS, J. L., and KIM, H. 1936. "Developmental studies of the pineapple, *Ananas comosus*. I. Origin and growth of leaves and inflorescence," *New Phytol.*, 35: 305–317.

KIERMAYER, OSWALD, 1959. "Gesteigerte Xylementwicklung bei *Solanum nigrum* durch Einfluss von Gibberellinsäure," *Deut. Bot. Gesell. Ber.*, 72: 343–348.

KONDRAT'EVA-MEL'VIL', E. A., 1957. "Obrazovanie kornevykh otpryskov u nekotorykh travyanistykh dvudol'nykh. [Formation of shoots on roots in some herbaceous dicotyledons.]" *Leningrad Univ. Vest. Ser. Biol.*, 12: 23–37.

KUMAZAWA, M., 1961. "Studies on the vascular course in maize plant," *Phytomorph.*, 11: 128–139.

LAMOTTE, C. E., and JACOBS, W. P., 1963. "A role of auxin in phloem regeneration in *Coleus* internodes," *Devlpmt. Biol.*, 8: 80–98.

LAUBENGAYER, R. A., 1949. "The vascular anatomy of the eight-rowed ear and tassel of Golden Bantam sweet corn," *Amer. J. Bot.*, 36: 236–244.

LAWALRÉE, ANDRÉ, 1948. "Histogénèse florale et végétative chez quelques Composées," *Cellule*, 52: 215–294.

LECLERQ, SUSANNE, 1951. "Étude morphologique et anatomique d'une fougère du Dévonien Supérieur. Le *Racophyton zygopteroides* nov. sp.," *Ann. Soc. Géol. Belgique*, 9: 1–62.

LÉGER, L. J., 1897. "Recherches sur l'origine et les transformations des éléments libériens," *Soc. Linn. Normandie, Mém.*, 19: 49–182.

LEHMBERG, K., 1923–1924. "Zur Kenntnis des Baues und der Entwicklung der wasserleitenden Bahnen bei der Sonnenblume (*Helianthus annuus*)," *Bot. Centbl. Beihefte*, 40: 183–236.

LEPPIK, E. E., 1961. "Phyllotaxis, anthotaxis and semataxis," *Acta Biotheor.*, 14: 1–28.

LINK, G. K. K., and EGGERS, V., 1946. "Mode, site, and time of initiation of hypocotyledonary bud primordia in *Linum usitatissimum* L." *Bot. Gaz.*, 107: 441–454.

LOISEAU, JEAN-EDME, 1959. "Observations et expérimentations sur la phyllotaxie et le functionnement du sommet végétatif chez quelques Balsaminacées," *Ann. des Sci. Nat., Bot.,* Sér. 11, **20**: 1–214.

LOUIS, J., 1935. "L'ontogénèse du système conducteur dans la pousse feuillée des Dicotylées et des Gymnospermes," *Cellule,* **44**: 87–172.

MAEDA, EIZO, 1962. "Structure and development of the vegetative shoot in rice plants," *Proc. Soc. Crop Plant Devlpmt., Fac. Agric., Nagoya Univ.,* **1**: 1–28.

MAHLBERG, P. G., 1960. "Embryogeny and histogenesis in *Nerium oleander* L. I. Organization of primary meristematic tissues," *Phytomorph.,* **10**: 118–131.

MAKSYMOWYCH, ROMAN, 1959. "Quantitative analysis of leaf development in *Xanthium pensylvanicum,*" *Amer. J. Bot.,* **46**: 635–644.

MANN, L. K., 1952. "Anatomy of the garlic bulb and factors affecting bulb development," *Hilgardia,* **21**: 195–251.

MARSDEN, M. P. F., and BAILEY, I. W., 1955. "A fourth type of nodal anatomy in dicotyledons illustrated by *Clerodendron trichotomum* Thunb.," *Arnold Arboretum J.,* **36**: 1–50.

MARTENS, P., 1950. "Le caractère "aphylle" des Rhyniales est-il primitif?" *Acad. Roy. des Sci. Belgique Brussels Cl. Sci. Bul.* Sér. 5, **36**: 811–822.

MASAYUKI, INOSAKA, 1962. "Studies on the development of vascular system in rice plant and the growth of each organ viewed from the vascular connection between them," *Miyazaki Univ. Fac. Agric. Bul.,* **7**: 15–116.

McGAHAN, M. W., 1955. "Vascular differentiation in the vegetative shoot of *Xanthium chinense,*" *Amer. J. Bot.,* **42**: 132–140.

MEYER, C. F., 1958. "Cell patterns in early embryogeny of the McIntosh apple," *Amer. J. Bot.,* **45**: 341–349.

MICHELINI, F. J., 1958. "The plastochron index in developmental studies of *Xanthium italicum* Moretti," *Amer. J. Bot.,* **45**: 525–533.

MILLENER, L. H., 1952. "An experimental demonstration of the dependence of phyllotaxis on rate of growth," *Nature,* **169**: 1052–1053.

MILLER, H. A., and WETMORE, R. H., 1945a. "Studies in the developmental anatomy of *Phlox drummondii* Hook. I. The embryo," *Amer. J. Bot.,* **32**: 588–599.

———, — ———, 1945b. "Studies in the developmental anatomy of *Phlox drummondii* Hook. II. The seedling," *Amer. J. Bot.,* **32**: 628–634.

———, — ———, 1946. "Studies in the developmental anatomy of *Phlox drummondii* Hook. III. The apices of the mature plant," *Amer. J. Bot.,* **33**: 1–10.

MILLER, R. H., 1958. "Morphology of *Humulus lupulus.* I. Developmental anatomy of the primary root," *Amer. J. Bot.,* **45**: 418–431.

MILLINGTON, W. F., and FISK, E. L., 1956. "Shoot development in *Xanthium pennsylvanicum.* I. The vegetative plant," *Amer. J. Bot.,* **43**: 655–665.

———, and GUNCKEL, J. E., 1950. "Structure and development of the vegetative shoot of *Liriodendron tulipifera* L.," *Amer. J. Bot.,* **37**: 326–335.

MITRA, G. C., and MAJUMDAR, G. P., 1952. "The leaf-base and the internode— their true morphology," *Paleobot.* **1**: 351–367.

MOENS, PAUL, 1963. "La vascularization de l'embryon et la plantule de *Coffea canephora* Pierre," *Cellule,* **64**: 71–126.

MOSELEY, M. F., 1961. "Morphological studies of the Nymphaeaceae. II. The flower of *Nymphaea*," *Bot. Gaz.*, **122**: 233–259.

MULLENDORE, NAOMI, 1948. "Seedling anatomy of *Brachypodium distachyum*," *Bot. Gaz.*, **109**: 341–348.

NAST, C. G., 1941. "The embryogeny and seedling morphology of *Juglans regia* L.," *Lilloa*, **6**: 163–205.

———, 1944. "The comparative morphology of the Winteraceae. VI. Vascular anatomy of the flowering shoot," *Arnold Arboretum J.*, **25**: 454–466.

NOZU, JOSHITOMO, 1956. "Anatomical and morphological studies in Japanese species of Ophioglossaceae. II. Rhizome and root," *Jap. J. Bot.*, **15**: 208–226.

ODHNOFF, CAMILLA, 1963. "The effect of gibberellin and phenyl-boric acid on xylem differentiation and epidermal cell elongation in bean roots," *Physiol. Plant.*, **16**: 474–483.

OGURA, Y., 1938. "Anatomie der Vegetationsorgane der Pteridophyten," *Handbuch der Pflanzenanatomie*, Vol. 7, Part 36.

O'NEILL, T. B., 1961. "Primary vascular organization of *Lupinus* shoot," *Bot. Gaz.*, **123**: 1–9.

ORSÓS, OTTO, 1941–1942. "Die Gewebeentwicklung bei der Kohlrabieknolle," *Flora*, **35**: 6–20.

OZENDA, PAUL, 1949. *Recherches sur les Dicotylédones apocarpiques. Contribution à l'étude des Angiospermes dites primitives*, Paris: Masson et Cie.

PARKE, R. V., 1963. "Initial vascularization of the vegetative shoot of *Abies concolor*," *Amer. J. Bot.*, **50**: 464–469.

PELLEGRINI, ORESTE, 1956. "Il differenziamento del procambio et l'organizzazione dell' epicotile nell' embriogenesi di alcune dicotiledoni," *Delpinoa*, **9**: 97–129.

PHILIPSON, W. R., 1946. "Studies in the development of the inflorescence. I. The capitulum of *Bellis perennis* L.," *Ann. Bot.*, **10**: 257–270.

———, 1947a. "Studies in the development of the inflorescence. II. The capitula of *Succisa pratensis* Moench. and *Dipsacus fullonum* L.," *Ann. Bot.*, **11**: 285–297.

———, 1947b. "Studies in the development of the inflorescence. III. The thyrse of *Valeriana officinalis* L.," *Ann. Bot.*, **11**: 409–416.

———, 1948. "Studies in the development of the inflorescence. IV. The capitula of *Hieracium boreale* Fries and *Dahlia gracilis* Ortg.," *Ann. Bot.*, **12**: 65–75.

———, 1949. "The ontogeny of the shoot apex in dicotyledons," *Biol. Rev.*, *Cambridge Phil. Soc.*, **24**: 21–50.

———, and BALFOUR, E. E., 1963. "Vascular patterns in dicotyledons," *Bot. Rev.*, **29**: 382–412.

PLANTEFOL, L., 1947. "Hélices foliaires, point végétatif et stèle chez les Dicotylédones. La notion de l'anneau initial," *Rev. Gén. de Bot.*, **54**: 49–80.

———, 1950. "La phyllotaxie," *Ann. Biol.*, **54**: 447–463.

PRAY, T. R., 1955a. "Foliar venation of angiosperms. II. Histogenesis of the venation of *Liriodendron*," *Amer. J. Bot.*, **42**: 18–27.

146 · BIBLIOGRAPHY

————, 1955b. "Foliar venation of angiosperms. IV. Histogenesis of the venation of *Hosta*," *Amer. J. Bot.*, **42**: 698–706.

————, 1960. "Ontogeny of the open dichotomous venation in the pinna of the fern *Nephrolepis*," *Amer. J. Bot.*, **47**: 319–328.

————, 1962. "Ontogeny of the closed dichotomous venation of *Regnellidium*," *Amer. J. Bot.*, **49**: 464–472.

————, 1963. "Origin of vein endings in angiosperm leaves," *Phytomorph.*, **13**: 60–81.

PRIESTLEY, J. H., and SCOTT, L. I., 1936. "The vascular anatomy of *Helianthus annuus* L.," *Leeds Phil. Soc. Proc.*, **3**: 159–173.

————, ——————, 1937. "Leaf venation and leaf trace in the monocotyledon," *Leeds Phil. Soc. Proc.*, **3**: 305–324.

————, ————, and GILLETT, E. C., 1935. "The development of the shoot in *Alstroemeria* and the unit of shoot growth in monocotyledons," *Ann. Bot.*, **49**: 161–179.

————, ————, and MATTINSON, K. M., 1937. "Dicotyledon phyllotaxis from the standpoint of development," *Leeds Phil. Soc. Proc.* **3**: 380–388.

REEVE, R. M., 1948a. "The "tunica-corpus" concept and development of shoot apices in certain dicotyledons," *Amer. J. Bot.*, **35**: 65–75.

————, 1948b. "Late embryogeny and histogenesis in *Pisum*," *Amer. J. Bot.*, **35**: 591–602.

REINHARD, ERNST, 1954. "Beobachtungen an in vitro cultivierten Geweben aus dem Vegetationskegel der *Pisum*-Wurzel," *Ztschr. f. Bot.*, **42**: 353–376.

————, 1956. "Ein Vergleich zwischen diarchen und triarchen Wurzeln von *Sinapis alba*," *Ztschr. f. Bot.*, **44**: 505–514.

————, 1960. "Über Rückregulierung des Gefässbündelmusters von *Sinapis alba*," *Deut. Bot. Gesell. Ber.*, **73**: 19–23.

RESH, ARMIN, 1959a–1959b. "Über Leptombündel und isolierte Siebröhren sowie deren Korrelationen zu den übrigen Leitungsbahnen in der Sprossachse," I. *Planta*, **52**: 467–489, II. *Planta*, **52**: 490–515.

RICHARDS, F. J., 1948. "The geometry of phyllotaxis and its origin", pp. 217–245 in "Growth in relation to differentiation and morphogenesis", *Symp. Soc. Expt. Biol.* No. 2.

————, 1956. "Spatial and temporal correlations involved in leaf pattern production at the apex," pp. 66–76 in F. L. Milthorpe (ed.), *The growth of leaves*, London: Butterworths Scientific Publications.

ROBERTS, L. W., 1960. "Experiments on xylem regeneration in stem wound responses in *Coleus*," *Bot. Gaz.*, **121**: 201–208.

————, and FOSKET, D. E., 1962. "Further experiments on wound-vessel formation in stem wounds of *Coleus*," *Bot. Gaz.*, **123**: 247–254.

RODIN, R. J., 1958. "Leaf anatomy of *Welwitschia*. I. Early development of the leaf," *Amer. J. Bot.*, **45**: 90–95.

ROHWEDER, OTTO, 1963. "Anatomische und histogenetische Untersuchungen an Laubsprossen und Blüten der Commelinaceen," *Bot. Jahrb.*, **82**: 1–99.

ROUSCHAL, ERNST, 1940. "Fluoreszenzoptische Messungen der Geschwindigkeit des Transpirationsstromes an krautigen Pflanzen mit Berücksichtigung der Blattspurflächen," *Flora*, **34**: 229–256.

RÜDIGER, WALTHER, 1953. "Eine Fasziation von *Euphrasia Odonites* L. mit markbürtiger Entstehung eines sekundären leptozentrischen Leitbündelzylinders," *Ztschr. f. Bot.*, **41**: 373–382.

SACHER, J. A., 1955a. "Cataphyll ontogeny in *Pinus lambertiana*," *Amer. J. Bot.*, **42**: 82–91.

———, 1955b. "Dwarf shoot ontogeny in *Pinus lambertiana*," *Amer. J. Bot.*, **42**: 784–792.

SARGENT, J. A., and WANGERMANN, E., 1959. "The effect of some growth regulators on the vascular system of *Lemna minor*," *New Phytol.*, **58**: 345–363.

SCHERER, P. E., 1904. "Studien über Gefässbündeltypen und Gefässformen," *Bot. Centbl., Beihefte*, **16**: 67–110.·

SCHOUTE, J. C., 1903. *Die Stelär-Theorie*, Jena: Gustav Fischer.

SCOTT, F. M., 1963. "Root hair zone of soil-grown roots," *Nature* [London], **199**: 1009–1010.

SCOTT, L. I., and PRIESTLEY, J. H., 1925. "Leaf and stem anatomy of *Tradescantia fluminensis*, Vell.," *Linn. Soc. London J., Bot.*, **47**: 1–28.

SHARMAN, B. C., 1942. "Developmental anatomy of the shoot of *Zea mays* L.," *Ann. Bot.*, **6**: 245–282.

SINNOTT, E. W., 1960. *Plant morphogenesis*, New York: McGraw-Hill.

SKIPWORTH, J. P., 1962. "The primary vascular system and phyllotaxis in *Hectorella caespitosa* Hook. f., *New Zealand J. Sci.*, **5**: 253–258.

SMITH, B. W., 1941. "The phyllotaxis of *Costus* from the standpoint of development," *Leeds Phil. Soc. Proc.*, **4**: 42–63.

SNOW, MARY, and SNOW, RICHARD, 1934. "The interpretation of phyllotaxis," *Biol. Rev., Cambridge Phil. Soc.*, **9**: 132–137.

———, ———, 1947. "On the determination of leaves," *New Phytol.*, **46**: 5–19.

———, ———, 1948. "On the determination of leaves," pp. 263–275 in "Growth in relation to differentiation and morphogenesis," *Symp. Soc. Expt. Biol. No. 2.*

SNOW, RICHARD, 1955. "Problems of phyllotaxis and leaf determination," *Endeavour*, **14**: 190–199.

SPORNE, K. R., 1958. "Some aspects of floral vascular systems," *Linn. Soc. London Proc.*, **169**: 75–84.

SPURR, A. R., 1949. "Histogenesis and organization of the embryo in *Pinus strobus* L.," *Amer. J. Bot.*, **36**: 629–641.

———, 1950. "Organization of the procambium and development of the secretory cells in the embryo of *Pinus strobus* L.," *Amer. J. Bot.*, **37**: 185–197.

STAFFORD, H. A., 1948. "Studies on the growth and xylary development of *Phleum pratense* seedlings in darkness and in light," *Amer. J. Bot.*, **35**: 706–715.

STEIN, D. B., and STEIN, O. L., 1960. "The growth of the stem of *Kalanchoë* cv. Brilliant Star," *Amer. J. Bot.*, **47**: 132–140.

STERLING, CLARENCE, 1945. "Growth and vascular development in the shoot apex of *Sequoia sempervirens* (Lamb.) Endl. II. Vascular development in relation to phyllotaxis," *Amer. J. Bot.*, 32: 380–386.

———, 1946. "Growth and vascular development in the shoot apex of *Sequoia sempervirens* (Lamb.) Endl. III. Cytological aspects of vascularization," *Amer. J. Bot.*, 33: 35–45.

———, 1947. "Organization of the shoot of *Pseudotsuga taxifolia* (Lamb.) Britt. II. Vascularization," *Amer. J. Bot.*, 34: 272–280.

———, 1949. "Embryonic differentiation in *Taxus cuspidata*," *Torrey Bot. Club Bul.*, 76: 116–133.

STEWARD, F. C., MAPES, M. O., and MEARS, K., 1958. "Growth and organized development in cultured cells. II. Organization in cultures grown from freely suspended cells," *Amer. J. Bot.*, 45: 705–708.

TANSLEY, A. G., 1907–1908. "Lectures on the evolution of the filicinean vascular system," *New Phytol.*, 6: 25–35; 53–68; 109–120; 135–147; 148–155; 187–203; 219–238; 253–269. 7: 1–16; 29–40.

TAYLOR, A. R. A., 1957. "Studies of the development of *Zostera marina* L. I. The embryo and seed," *Canad. J. Bot.*, 35: 477–499.

THIBAULT, MONIQUE, 1946. "Contribution à l'étude des radicelles de carotte," *Rev. Gén. Bot.*, 53: 434–460.

THOMPSON, N. P., and HEIMSCH, C., 1964. "Stem anatomy and aspects of development in tomato," *Amer. J. Bot.*, 51: 7–19.

TORREY, J. G., 1951. "Cambial formation in isolated pea roots following decapitation," *Amer. J. Bot.*, 38: 596–604.

———, 1953. "The effect of certain metabolic inhibitors on vascular tissue differentiation in isolated pea roots," *Amer. J. Bot.*, 40: 525–533.

———, 1954. "The role of vitamins and micronutrient elements in the nutrition of the apical meristem of pea roots," *Plant Physiol.*, 29: 279–287.

———, 1955. "On the determination of vascular patterns during tissue differentiation in excised pea roots," *Amer. J. Bot.*, 42: 183–198.

———, 1957. "Auxin control of vascular pattern formation in regenerating pea root meristems grown in vitro," *Amer. J. Bot.*, 44: 859–870.

———, 1963. "Cellular patterns in developing roots," pp. 285–314 in "Cell Differentiation", *Symp. Soc. Expt. Biol.* No. 17.

TRÉCUL, A., 1881. "Recherches sur l'ordre d'apparition des premiers vaisseaux dans les organes aériens," *Ann. des Sci. Nat., Bot.*, Sér. VI, 12: 251–381.

TROLL, W., and RAUH, W., 1950. "Das Erstarkungswachstum krautiger Dikotylen, mit besonderer Berücksichtigung der primären Verdickungsvorgänge," *Sitzber. Heidelberg. Akad. Wiss., Math. Nat. Kl.* Abh. 1, 86 p.

TUCKER, S. C., 1961. "Phyllotaxis and vascular organization of the carpels in *Michelia fuscata*," *Amer. J. Bot.*, 48: 60–71.

———, 1962. "Ontogeny and phyllotaxis of the terminal vegetative shoots of *Michelia fuscata*," *Amer. J. Bot.*, 49: 722–737.

———, 1963. "Development and phyllotaxis of the vegetative axillary bud of *Michelia fuscata*," *Amer. J. Bot.*, 50: 661–668.

VAN FLEET, D. S., 1961. "Histochemistry and function of the endodermis," *Bot. Rev.*, **27**: 165–220.

VAN ITERSON, G., 1907. *Mathematische und mikroskopisch-anatomische Studien über Blattstellungslehre,* Jena: Gustav Fischer.

VAN TIEGHEM, PH., 1882. "Sur quelques points de l'anatomie des Cucurbitacées," *Soc. Bot. France Bul.,* **29**: 277–283.

————, and DOULIOT, H., 1886. "Sur la polystélie," *Ann. des Sci. Nat., Bot.,* Sér. 7, **3**: 275–322.

VAUGHAN, J. G., 1955. "The morphology and growth of the vegetative and reproductive apices of *Arabidopsis thaliana* (L.) Heynh., *Capsella bursa-pastoris* (L.) Medic. and *Anagallis arvensis* L.," *Linn. Soc. London J., Bot.,* **55**: 279–301.

WARDLAW, C. W., 1943a. "Experimental and analytical studies of pteridophytes I. Preliminary observations on the development of buds on the rhizome of the ostrich fern (*Matteuccia struthiopteris* Tod.)," *Ann. Bot.,* **7**: 171–184.

————, 1943b. "Experimental and analytical studies of pteridophytes. II. Experimental observations on the development of buds in *Onoclea sensibilis* and in species of *Dryopteris,*" *Ann. Bot.,* **7**: 357–377.

————, 1944. "Experimental and analytical studies of pteridophytes. IV. Stelar morphology: Experimental observations on relation between leaf development and stelar morphology in species of *Dryopteris* and *Onoclea,*" *Ann. Bot.,* **8**: 387–399.

————, 1945. "Experimental and analytical studies of pteridophytes. V. Stelar morphology: The development of the vascular system," *Ann. Bot.,* **9**: 217–233.

————, 1946a. "Experimental and analytical studies of pteridophytes. VII. Stelar morphology: The effect of defoliation on the stele of *Osmunda* and *Todea,*" *Ann. Bot.,* **9**: 97–107.

————, 1946b. "Experimental and analytical studies of pteridophytes. IX. The effect of removing leaf primordia on the development of *Angiopteris evecta* Hoffm.," *Ann. Bot.,* **10**: 223–235.

————, 1947. "Experimental investigations of the shoot apex of *Dryopteris aristata* Druce.," *Roy. Soc. London Phil. Trans B.,* **232**: 343–384.

————, 1949a. "Experimental and analytical studies of pteridophytes. XIV. Leaf formation and phyllotaxis in *Dryopteris aristata* Druce.," *Ann. Bot.,* **13**: 163–198.

————, 1949b. "Experiments on organogenesis in ferns," *Growth Symp.,* **9**: 93–131.

————, 1950. "Experimental and analytical studies of pteridophytes. XVI. The induction of leaves and buds in *Dryopteris aristata* Druce.," *Ann. Bot.,* **14**: 435–455.

————, 1952. *Phylogeny and morphogenesis. Contemporary aspects of botanical science,* London: Macmillan.

————, 1956. "Experimental and analytical studies of pteridophytes. XXXII. Further investigations on the effect of undercutting fern leaf primordia," *Ann. Bot.,* **20**: 121–132.

———, 1957. "Experimental and analytical studies of pteridophytes. XXXVII. A note on the inception of microphylls and macrophylls," *Ann. Bot.*, **83:** 427–437.

———, and Cutter, E. G., 1956. "Experimental and analytical studies of pteridophytes. XXXI. The effect of shallow incisions on organogenesis in *Dryopteris aristata* Druce.," *Ann. Bot.*, **22:** 39–56.

Warren Wilson, P. M., and Warren Wilson, J., 1961. "Cambium formation in wounded solanaceous stems," *Ann. Bot.*, **25:** 104–115.

Weaver, H. L., 1960. "Vascularization of the root-hypocotyl-cotyledon axis of *Glycine max* (L.) Merrill," *Phytomorph.*, **10:** 82–86.

West, C., 1917. "A contribution to the study of the Marattiaceae," *Ann. Bot.*, **31:** 361–414.

Wetmore, R. H., 1943. "Leaf-stem relationships in the vascular plants," *Torreya*, **43:** 16–28.

———, and Rier, J. P., 1963. "Experimental induction of vascular tissues in callus of angiosperms," *Amer. J. Bot.*, **50:** 418–430.

———, and Sorokin, S., 1955. "On the differentiation of xylem," *Arnold Arboretum J.*, **36:** 305–317.

———, and Wardlaw, C. W., 1951. "Experimental morphogenesis in vascular plants," *Ann. Rev. Plant Physiol.*, **2:** 269–292.

Wilcox, Hugh, 1954. "Primary organization of active and dormant roots of noble fir, *Abies procera*," *Amer. J. Bot.*, **41:** 812–821.

———, 1962a. "Growth studies of the root of incense cedar, *Libocedrus decurrens*. I. The origin and development of primary tissues," *Amer. J. Bot.*, **49:** 221–236.

———, 1962b. "Growth studies of the root of incense cedar, *Libocedrus decurrens*. II. Morphological features of the root system and growth behavior," *Amer. J. Bot.*, **49:** 237–245.

———, 1964. "Xylem in roots of *Pinus resinosa* Ait. in relation to heterorhizy and growth activity," pp. 457–478 in M. H. Zimmermann (ed.), *The formation of wood in forest trees*, New York: Academic Press.

index

index

153